Healthy Recipes
for Your
Nutritional Type

Healthy Recipes for Your Nutritional Type

By Dr. Joseph Mercola and Dr. Kendra Pearsall

Publisher: Mercola.com Health Resources, LLC
3200 West Higgins Road
Hoffman Estates, IL 60169

Illustrations: Marcie Bringardner, Allen Berlinski

Publisher's Note: This book is intended as a reference volume only, not as a medical manual. The ideas, procedures, and suggestions contained herein are not intended as a substitute for consultation with your personal medical practitioner. Neither the publisher nor the authors shall be liable or responsible for any loss or damage allegedly arising from any information or suggestion in this book. Further, if you suspect that you have a medical problem, we urge you to seek professional medical help.

This book may be bulk ordered at special rates.
Contact customerservice@mercola.com or write to
Mercola.com Health Resources, LLC, 3200 West Higgins Road,
Hoffman Estates, IL 60169

Printed in the United States of America

Healthy Recipes for Your Nutritional Type

Dr. Joseph Mercola

with

Dr. Kendra Degen Pearsall

Contents

Vegetables   **97**

Grains   **119**

Healthy Recipes for Your Nutritional Type

This cookbook, *Healthy Recipes for Your Nutritional Type*, is an off-spring of my book *Take Control of Your Health*. I wrote Take Control of Your Health as a one-stop resource for achieving overall, optimal health in a natural way. I wanted you to have a simple-to-follow, complete guide for transforming your health physically, emotionally, and spiritually.

Our current medical model is designed to merely treat the symptoms of illness—without determining the underlying causes. Unfortunately, you're often prescribed medication after expensive medication, creating more symptoms or side effects that require even more medication. Before you know it, you're sicker than when you first went to the doctor.

For thirty years, it's been my mission to help people break that cycle of dependence on damaging and sometimes even fatal consequences of the current medical model.

Most health problems are a result of an unhealthy lifestyle. *Take Control of Your Health* shows you the principles of healthy living—how to make natural lifestyle changes to restore and revitalize your body. At the heart of *Take Control of Your Health* is the importance of proper nutrition. It's my belief that many of today's health problems started when we moved away from the natural eating and lifestyle habits of our long-ago ancestors.

In my practice and through my website, I've repeatedly seen the miraculous healing power of nutrition. Simple dietary changes can reverse even chronic degenerative diseases of both the mind and body. I'm not saying these changes happened overnight and I'm not advocating any quick fixes here. What I am saying is, with education, encouragement, and determination, you have the ability to achieve health independence and wellbeing.

Through many years of studying, researching, and working with top nutritionists, I developed Nutritional Typing. It's what I believe to be the healthiest, smartest, and simplest way for people to obtain the greatest benefit from what they eat.

At my clinic The Optimal Wellness Center outside of Chicago, I encourage all of my patients to be analyzed for their own unique

Introduction

Nutritional Type. This is important because each one of us has a unique genetic makeup allowing our bodies to metabolize foods optimally. Your personal nutritional analysis will place you into one of three categories: Protein Type, Carb Type, or Mixed Type. Understanding which type you are allows you to choose foods that are the most healing and beneficial for your unique metabolism.

Once you start eating for your individual Nutritional Type, you'll see amazing changes taking place in your body. You'll have more energy than you've ever had before, you'll move effortlessly toward your ideal weight, your health will improve, and you'll feel better than you can probably ever remember feeling.

With the development and success of Nutritional Typing, it was natural for my patients and readers to want recipe ideas to make eating for their individual types easier. That's how *Healthy Recipes for Your Nutritional Type* was born—this is a collection of healthy, nutritious, and satisfying recipes specifically designed for your unique Nutritional Type.

Making changes in your diet doesn't have to be boring or difficult. You can take control of your health—and create nutritionally sound, healthy, and delicious meals along the way.

Chapter 1

Discover the Powerful Health-Building Value of Nutritional Typing and Eating Right for Your Nutritional Type

Many may not realize that I was not raised in a home that taught me any nutritional basics. I love my mother dearly, but she was caught up hook, line, and sinker in the conventional thoughts of what was healthy. My mother never graduated high school and worked nights, weekends, and most holidays as a waitress. So what that meant was that we frequently relied on highly processed foods for our meals which could be heated up long after she left to go to work.

My mom also made sure there were plenty of snacks at home, and I had my fair share of cookies, Pop Tarts, and Hostess Twinkies. Breakfast usually consisted of cereal and perhaps white bread toast loaded with margarine, sugar, and cinnamon. I continued the toast and margarine practice into my early medical school days, but I did substitute whole wheat bread for the white bread—and believed I was doing well.

Except for fruit, I rarely had raw food. I clearly remember one of my friends in college eating a raw pepper, and I was aghast as I thought he would surely get sick. My friend assured me this was a healthy practice and encouraged me to consider it.

This was about the time I began to explore the importance of nutrition with a subscription to *Prevention* magazine and a series of books written by nutrition pioneer Adelle Davis.

Later I studied Nathan Pritikin, who convinced me of the importance of a diet that was high in carbohydrates and fiber and low in fat and protein. Later, I became further confused by reading and trying the *Fit For Life* diet in the late '80s. Unfortunately, as a Protein Type (I'll explain what this is later) neither diet was designed for my Nutritional Type. Instead, they worsened my health. The "fruit only" breakfast that *Fit For Life* advocates quickly increased my triglycerides to over 1000, so I stopped that one relatively quickly.

In my attempts to be healthy, I ate the low-fat, low-protein, high-carb diet that Pritikin recommended. This was great for a Carb Type but a disaster for a Protein Type. For 20 years, my diet consisted of mostly vegetarian meals such as uncooked oats with water (I thought this was healthier than cooked oatmeal), plenty of whole wheat bread, white rice, tubs of margarine, beans, and produce.

This approach, combined with my running of up to 50 miles or more per week, plummeted my total cholesterol level to 75, and this was without any drugs like Lipitor. At that time, most physicians (including myself) felt the lower your cholesterol, the better. Of course, this was not correct and was actually causing health problems for me, as an optimal total cholesterol level is around 175 to 200.

One of the primary problems with low cholesterol levels is that your body requires cholesterol as a building block to build the vast majority of your hormones. It is a foundational precursor to nearly all of your steroid hormones, and when it is low, your hormones will become unbalanced.

Even though many often told me I looked gaunt and too thin, I tried to evangelize my fellow med students, patients, and anyone who would listen to eat this same way.

In medical school we had a system where the 100 students in our class would rotate and take very comprehensive notes so we would only have to do take notes a few times a quarter, yet we would have everyone's comprehensive notes. This helped us study and pass our exams.

When it was my turn to take notes, no matter what the topic was, I would find a way to insert nutritional advice into the student notes. This earned me the nickname "Dr. Fiber" for my recommendation of high fiber, high-grain diets.

During my three years of family practice residency, I frequently gave free nutrition lectures. However, they weren't well attended, and the interest was minimal. But my enthusiasm for the high-carb, low-fat diet came to a screeching halt one fateful night when I attended a lecture by Dr. Ron Rosedale in Chicago in the fall of 1995. Dr. Rosedale opened up my eyes to how high-carb diets had the potential to increase insulin to abnormally high levels. Furthermore, he taught that keeping insulin levels in the normal range was central to optimal health and keeping disease at bay.

Eat Right for Your Blood Type Caused Me to Have Diabetes

After I understood insulin, I took another sidetrack with Dr. Peter D'Adamo's *Eat Right for Your Blood Type* book, which appealed to me because it preached the individualization of diet based on one's blood type. There are four basic blood types, O, A, B, and AB, and so four different diets are offered. Dr. D'Adamo's dietary recommendations can help to some extent—primarily because he encourages his readers to stay away from refined and processed foods and to eat whole, fresh organic foods instead.

Additionally, the most common blood type is O, and in this system, blood type O's are instructed to avoid wheat and minimize consumption of almost all other grain products.

My experience has taught me that most people do tend to improve once they make these changes, so it is my impression that these were the primary reasons why some people had some success with the Blood Type Diet. Unfortunately, my blood type is A and that diet is high in grains and low in meat. This is the exact opposite of what a Protein Type like me should be eating to stay healthy. While trying this approach to diet, my fasting blood sugar rose to over 126. This means I actually developed type 2 diabetes from following this program.

This is not unusual considering 75 million people in the United States alone have diabetes and pre-diabetes, and nearly all of my paternal relatives have diabetes or have died from diabetic complications. So, I immediately got the clue and stopped D'Adamo's Blood Type A Diet. Although I am grateful to him for bringing attention to the concept of diet individualization, I have reached the conclusion that there is a far more important factor than just your general blood type that can help you determine what foods are best for you.

And that factor is *your metabolism*. Your blood type has absolutely *no* direct influence on your metabolism of protein, carbs, and fats for energy. And energy metabolism is the key issue of health.

Once I started recommending that my patients decrease the amount of carbs in their diets I noticed most of them experienced dramatic improvements in their insulin levels and overall health. I was so impressed with these results that I wrote a book about my experience called *The No Grain Diet*, which eventually became a *New York Times* bestselling book.

However, there were still a fair number of people who did not get better with the diet that I told all my patients to follow—despite their strict compliance. I couldn't understand why.

My Experience With Vegetable Juicing

Right around the time of my experimentation with the blood type, I was very impressed with how healthy a few of my older patients were. There was one 70-year-old woman who had followed nutritional principles for many years, and she looked like she was 40. She believed it was due to her vegetable juicing program. So, I started to research this and was impressed with the benefits of raw food vegetable juicing. I started doing it myself and recommending it to many of my patients.

Fortunately, I had never really struggled with any serious health issues and have, for the most part, felt full of energy my entire life. So, I was unable to appreciate any side effects from juicing other than starting to become allergic to some of the vegetables I was juicing on a regular basis (like Swiss chard and collard greens).

It wasn't until I learned Metabolic Typing that I would understand that the juicing would move my biochemistry in the exact opposite way I needed it to go. It was far too high in potassium for my needs and actually sped up my already far too fast oxidation rate.

However, this type of vegetable juicing was beyond phenomenal for many of the patients I recommended it to, and they had enormous benefits. Later I realized those who benefited were the Carb Types. But my experience with many patients not improving with juicing made me far more open to the Metabolic Typing principles that I would learn in a few years.

The juicing program I developed back then is still used in our clinic and is one of the more popular pages on my Website. Mercola.com has ranked number one or two for the term "vegetable juicing" on Google for the past five years. We still strongly recommend that all of our Carb Type patients adopt this juicing plan to achieve a high level of health.

The positive benefits many of my patients experienced with vegetable juicing helped convince me of the importance of raw food and really set the stage for my future experimentation with raw animal foods.

My Next Nutritional Health Epiphany—Metabolic Typing™

Dr. Rosedale's insights on insulin were finally some of the nutritional golden truths that I had been searching for, for so many years. Nothing I have learned since then has altered or changed my views of these truths. In fact, it has been quite the contrary. Most people normalizing their insulin levels have experienced profound improvements in their health.

The next stop on my nutritional journey occurred in early 2001 when I finally understood the reason that a significant number of people did not respond to the insulin-control program I had developed. That is when I encountered Bill Wolcott's book *The Metabolic Typing Diet*, which carefully explained that there are three basic types of human metabolism:

- Carb Type metabolism

- Protein Type metabolism

- Mixed Type metabolism

People metabolize the food they eat in different ways based mostly on their genetics, but a number of other factors, such as chronic stress, can also influence our metabolic activity. According to Metabolic Typing, people can be classified as either Carb Types, Protein Types, or Mixed Types, based on how they answer a computerized questionnaire. Also, there are two different kinds of Carb Types, two different kinds of Protein Types, and two different kinds of Mixed Types.

Discovering Metabolic Typing was a major epiphany for me and explained the years of frustration I was having in trying to fit everyone into the same nutritional model.

There Is No Perfect Diet For Everyone

Once I adopted Metabolic Typing into my practice, the patients who previously had not responded well to our program started to improve. I will be eternally grateful to Bill Wolcott for revolutionizing the way I practiced medicine. It is my belief that Metabolic Typing and understanding the importance of insulin control are the two most important principles of successful nutrition counseling. In my opinion, they are both deserving of the nutritional equivalent of the Nobel Prize.

I had previously recommended fresh organic vegetable juice to everyone, but realized after learning about Metabolic Typing that this has the greatest value for Carb Types, has less value for most Mixed Types and has the least value for Protein Types. Metabolic Typing helped me finally understand that the high protein, low-carb diet I had been advocating as a starting point to all of my patients to normalize insulin levels was a disaster for Carb Types. These people actually needed a dietary approach that was closer to what Pritikin advised.

Now, it's important to understand that I didn't abandon all of the nutritional principles I had acquired prior to learning about Metabolic Typing, such as eating lots of fresh, raw, organic, whole foods. My team and I actually incorporated this strong emphasis on food quality at the very beginning of our practice of Metabolic Type nutrition.

We also made the discovery (after just a few months of practicing Metabolic Type nutrition) that it is not enough to make the right food choices. It's equally important to eat your foods—at each meal—in the right order!

For instance, which food do you think would be the best one for Protein Types to eat first at any given meal—meat or a vegetable? Which food do you think would be the best one for Carb Types to eat first at any given meal—meat or a vegetable? And, which food do you think would be the best one for Mixed Types to eat first at any given meal—meat or a vegetable?

Protein Types should eat their meat first, Carb Types should eat their vegetable first, and Mixed Types should eat their meat and vegetable together! When this is faithfully practiced, digestive and metabolic efficiency typically improves dramatically. This is indicated by:

- Improved meal satisfaction (and with smaller portions of food)

- No need for snacks in between meals

- No more food cravings

Over the course of the five years we have been using Metabolic Typing, we have identified what is most valuable about the system that we started with. We have eliminated what is unnecessary and burdensome, and came up with big nutritional improvements that have helped our patients often experience dramatic and even amazing improvements in their health—often within the first month of eating right for their Nutritional Type.

When I told other clinicians who were doing Metabolic Typing with their patients how we had improved the Metabolic Type nutrition plans, I was surprised to hear that they were all eager to learn about what we were doing. This was because many of them had actually stopped using Metabolic Typing in their practice. Why? Because it was simply too complex and burdensome for the average patient to successfully implement.

Our experience with thousands of patients has confirmed for us, over and over again, that we have identified the most important nutritional principles that help people to achieve dramatically improved health, without burdensome effort.

Raw Food Evolution

After I had become comfortable with Metabolic Typing, I learned more about the Weston Price Foundation with Sally Fallon and Mary Enig. Their compelling literature started my raw food exploration by using raw dairy. It took nearly two years to locate an Amish farmer in Michigan who could drive dairy to my Chicago-area clinic, but it was well worth the wait. I observed yet another improvement boost among many of our patients who were able to access raw, unpasteurized dairy.

From there, I progressed to one of the only teachers of *raw animal foods*, Aajonus Vanderplanitz. Vanderplanitz teaches that humans are the only species that cooks their meat. All other animals eat their food and meat raw. Vanderplanitz was able to recover from some very serious medical problems by eating a raw food diet and he has helped many people do the same.

While I don't agree with everything that Vanderplanitz teaches, especially his liberal use of raw honey, he has uncovered many helpful principles and his work is part of our new system called Nutritional Typing.

Distinctions Between Metabolic Typing (MT) and Nutritional Typing (NT)

Simplified Categorization

MT categorizes people into three main metabolic types, but there are six subtypes and nine possible Metabolic Typing combinations. In our experience though, all you really need to know is whether you are you a Protein Type, Carb Type, or Mixed Type.

Food Quality

One of the most important distinctions between these two systems has to do with attention to food quality. For example, MT emphasizes specific foods to eat but does not strongly emphasize the quality of these foods. On the other hand, NT advocates that buying the highest quality food that is available to you is vital. Not only do we advise and help our patients obtain fresh, locally grown, organic food, but we also recommend that you eat as much of your food raw as possible. Eating raw will serve to preserve the nutritional integrity of your food.

If you do cook your food, and we know that most people will, then it is very important to use our low-temperature cooking guidelines as often as possible, as this will minimize the amount of heat damage that you cause to your food.

You might already be familiar with the differences between raw and pasteurized milk. Well, similarly, if you cook (heat damage) other foods, they will lose much of their ability to transfer their vital energy to your body.

Supplementation

MT advocates that everyone should take a number of supplements (multi-vitamins, enzymes, and other products) designed for their type. However, NT does not focus on nutritional supplementation as a primary means of improving your health. The primary approach is to use food, and rely on supplements only when indicated for specialized conditions.

Overall Nutritional Differences

MT nutrition plans emphasize making the right food choices based not only on whether you're a Protein, Carb, or Mixed Type, but also takes into account your endocrine type and, yes, even your blood type (although the list of blood-type-related foods to avoid are much shorter and different than what Dr. D'Adamo teaches).

MT also emphasizes that you should be focused on the percentages and ratios of protein, carbs, and fat that you are eating at each meal. (It's not surprising that many of our patients became confused when we were practicing this approach.)

In NT, the emphasis is on making the right food choices for your basic type—Protein, Carb, or Mixed—together with a big emphasis on food quality and eating foods raw. Plus, emphasis is placed on the best ways to cook your food, if you are going to cook it, and always consuming your most metabolically important food or foods *first*, thereby practicing the right kind of food combining for your Nutritional Type. Last but not least, eating consciously is an incredibly important facet of NT.

This is all much easier to do and, we feel, far more effective at improving your digestive and metabolic efficiency than focusing on making food choices based on three different, and sometimes contradictory, concerns (Metabolic Type, endocrine type, and blood type)—not to mention also having to focus on the percentages and ratios of protein, carbs, and fat that you are eating at each meal while taking lots of supplements.

Also, we strongly prefer the term "Nutritional Typing," over "Metabolic Typing" because the emphasis is on *nutrition*. And, ultimately Nutritional or Metabolic Typing is only a means to an end, which is: knowing how to truly nourish yourself in the way that you need to be nourished.

I have collaborated with nearly half a dozen leading nutrition experts who were trained in Metabolic Typing, who also felt the system needed to be revised and simplified. We have developed our own system for determining whether you are a Protein, Carb, or Mixed Type and this revolutionary, cutting-edge, refinement was developed in the spring of 2007. It is literally hot off the press.

This information does not exist in written form *anywhere* else in the world. It is my belief that helping develop and provide an easy system for individualizing your ideal diet may be the single most important contribution I ever made. The potential for this program to improve your health is beyond extraordinary. It has been our observation that most of the people who faithfully apply NT observe phenomenal improvements in their health.

Why Do You Need Nutritional Typing?

Your Nutritional Type determines your individual nutritional requirements and dictates your individual responses to what you eat and drink. Foods and individual nutrients do not behave the same way in people with different Nutritional Types.

So, what exactly is your Nutritional Type?

Your nutritional type is primarily determined by your genetically inherited ability to metabolize various foods into the energy and building blocks your body needs to be healthy. However, environmental influences, such as stress, can cause a functional adaptation in your metabolism that temporarily overrides your genetics. Ultimately, your Nutritional Type, at any given time in your life, is determined by identifying the primary characteristics of your metabolism. And identifying your basic Nutritional Type is really quite simple because there are only three basic types: Protein Types, Carb Types, and Mixed Types. While there can be significant variations within each one of these three basic types, everyone on this planet, at any given time, will have a Protein, Carb, or Mixed Type metabolism.

Why Nutritional Typing is Not Just Another Fad Diet

Tens of thousands of books have been written on dieting and nutrition in the past 100 years, each one with its own principles and teachings. Sometimes the diets seem to work, other times not, and often they help one person but are devastating to another. For example, some people feel great on the Atkins Diet (low-carb) and quickly lose excess weight. Meanwhile, other people have reported feeling sick, tired, or moody, and have gained weight on a low-carb diet.

Unfortunately, nearly all of the dietary recommendations that you read or hear promote a single regimen or approach as being ideal or appropriate for everyone who applies it. Remember that I have made this mistake too—several times. And this is a terrible mistake in that it completely fails to appreciate the proven fact that we do not all have the same nutritional requirements. Certain foods or a diet that works well for one person may actually cause health problems for someone else. Unfortunately, this profound truth is not "officially" acknowledged by the vast majority of doctors, dieticians, nutritionists, and other health care practitioners. And it took me years to learn this for myself.

We have all been subjected to general and often vague food recommendations by so-called experts, even though it has been over 2,000 years since the ancient Roman philosopher Lucretius observed the profound truth that "What is food to one man may be fierce poison to others." (Over the years, this statement was re-phrased, and in modern times it is most commonly known as, "One man's food is another man's poison.")

Just as you are unique in regard to your outward physical characteristics, you also are unique with respect to your inner biochemistry and physiology. There is actually a spectrum of possible variations that exist in the way people digest and metabolize foods.

When it comes to digestion and metabolism, however, there is much that you also have in common with others. For instance, we all need to be able to digest and metabolize protein. What makes NT so different from any other "diet" you may have tried is that it guides you to the foods that are the right sources of protein for you, together with teaching you how to optimize the metabolic value of the protein.

Remember, what's right for you could be very wrong for someone else, because we do have our differences—and it's our differences that make us unique.

The Details Are Important

Granted, our differences are mostly in the details, but never underestimate the importance of details. You may not have thought much about the nutritional differences between the white meat and dark meat of poultry, but in Nutritional Typing, it is known that there is a significant difference in the value of these two foods.

Here is a prime example of how a small detail can make a big difference. The molecular formula for hemoglobin (which is the part of a red blood cell that picks up and carries oxygen) is

C738H1166FeN203O208S2 (C=Carbon, H=Hydrogen, Fe=Iron, N=Nitrogen, O=Oxygen, and S=Sulfur). Hemoglobin is a molecule containing 2,318 atoms, and *only one* of those atoms is iron. Compared to the entire structure of hemoglobin, the one atom of iron could be viewed as a very minor detail. But that one very minor detail makes it possible for the cells of your body to receive the oxygen they need, without which, of course, you would die.

So the lesson here is: never take the details for granted!

Nutritional Typing gives more attention to the specific details of what you are eating than any other school of nutrition, diet book, or fad diet in history! And you will want to give faithful attention to the details that we teach you once you experience the benefits of doing so.

It is Highly Likely You Have Never Experienced Optimal Health

It may sound shocking, but it's absolutely true. It's likely that you haven't yet experienced optimum health. What does optimum health feel like? It's:

• Having more energy than you know what to do with

• Being free from aches and pains

• Feeling happy, optimistic, and at peace emotionally

Being optimally healthy means that you feel this way almost always, as opposed to feeling this way only rarely when you're having a "good day."

It is not your fault, though, that you likely haven't reached this level of health. Our culture is intertwined with pervasive corporate interests that are directly aligned with their self-serving profit motives. It is designed to make these companies successful, often at the expense of people's long-term health.

NT Shows You How to Use Food as Your Medicine

Part of what our culture promotes is a medical system based on treating symptoms, and not addressing the underlying cause of those symptoms. Because of this, conventional medicine, although highly effective for many acute health challenges, really has a very limited ability to resolve most chronic illnesses. Therapeutically, this approach or paradigm is known as allopathic medicine.

If you want a powerful visual analogy of this concept, please view the seven-minute animation I created a few years ago that demonstrates this. You can see it at:

www.mercola.com/allopath

Unfortunately, much of contemporary alternative medicine falls under the same strategic approach. This stems from the lack of technology to effectively analyze and resolve the biochemical imbalances that are the underlying cause of disease.

This is not so with NT, however. Nutritional Typing is unlike conventional medicine and most alternative medicine modalities in its unique ability to:

- Balance your total body chemistry

- Address disease processes at their causative level

- Prevent illness

- Rebuild health

- Provide uniquely long-lasting health benefits

When you begin eating right for your Nutritional Type, you will also begin to move toward metabolic balance. And as you move toward metabolic balance, your body will be producing energy more efficiently from the foods that you're eating.

When you are in metabolic balance, you will then discover what it feels like to be truly healthy. You will have created an inner environment that is conducive to you experiencing your highest levels of:

- Peaceful energy

- Relaxed alertness

- Emotional poise

- Positive stable mood

- Great mental clarity

NT works for those who are healthy and those who are experiencing health challenges. If your body is in need of healing, you will be helping yourself realize your full healing potential. If you feel that you are already healthy, you're in for a surprise! You will create the possibility of truly knowing just how healthy you can be.

How Will I Know I'm Eating Right for My Nutritional Type?

You will experience a profound difference in the way you feel before and after you begin eating right for your Nutritional Type. When you are *not* eating right for your Nutritional Type, you typically:

- Do not feel satisfied with your meals

- Have cravings, especially for sugar

- Have frequent and intense hunger (especially true for Protein Types)

- Experience mood swings

- Experience some degree of "brain fog"

- Have inconsistent and/or low energy

- Are more prone to feeling anxious and depressed

- Are more prone to addictions

- Will be very prone to being overweight or underweight

- Are prone to all types of degenerative processes

Meanwhile, at the other end of the spectrum, when you *are* eating right for your Nutritional Type you typically:

- Will be more satisfied with your meals

- Can go for longer periods without eating

- Are completely *free* from *all* cravings

- Experience a more positive and stable mood

- Experience elimination of "brain fog" and heightened levels of mental clarity

- Experience more consistently good energy

- Lose weight if you are overweight and gain weight if you are underweight

- Support on-going cellular repair and regeneration

- Begin to realize your full health potential

The Principles of Nutritional Typing

There are five primary principles that you will need to focus on to successfully eat right for your Nutritional Type. The first three principles are actually of equal importance, but we will list them here in the order that they will need to be addressed as you shop, plan, and prepare your meals:

1. Make the right food choices. Initially, choose all of your foods from your Nutritional Type food chart. Buy the best quality food that is available to you.

2. Consider what you will eat *raw* and what you will eat *cooked*. When cooking, *never* overcook your food. Use low temperature cooking as often as you can.

3. Always consume your most metabolically important food or foods *first*! For example, if you are a Protein Type, eat your meat first. If you are a Carb Type, eat your vegetables first. And if you are a Mixed Type, eat your meat and vegetables together.

4. Practice the right kind of food combining for your Nutritional Type. (This is especially important for *Mixed* Types.)

5. Eat consciously! Pay attention to what you are eating and—if you do not already do so—then begin to practice eating slowly and chewing your food thoroughly.

    When you put these five principles into practice, you then set yourself up for success with principle number six, which has to do with those perplexing percentages and ratios of protein, carbs, and fat that you are eating at each meal.

6. Don't worry about percentages and ratios. The amounts of protein, fat and carbohydrates that you are eating at each meal are definitely important—**but please do not think about this in**

terms of percentages and ratios. The amount of protein, fat, and carbs that you eat is also known as the macronutrient ratio, and it is the most dynamic part of eating right for your Nutritional Type. But, the correct macronutrient ratio for you can vary depending on a number of factors, including your levels of stress and activity, and also the climate where you are living.

Perhaps you have heard about the macronutrient ratio, as it is the subject of a book called "The Zone Diet." This book proposes that to get in the "zone" a person should strive to eat 40 percent of their calories from carbs, 30 percent from protein, and 30 percent from fat.

However, this is incredibly misleading, as there is *no* macronutrient ratio that is right for everyone all the time. (It's another one-size-fits-all approach.) As indicated above, even your own ideal macronutrient ratio can vary significantly from time to time.

So how do you get your ideal amounts of protein, fat, and carbs right at every meal without turning your meal into a complex mathematical problem?

The answer is simple: Focus on making the right food choices (principle number 1) and eating your food in the right way (principles 2, 3, 4, and 5). As for how much you should eat of any given food in your meal plan, initially, you should let your appetite be your guide, and then learn from your experience. You must always listen carefully to your body, trust what it tells you, and remember what you have learned.

If you pay attention, your own body language (how you feel physically, mentally and emotionally) will always let you know if you are or are not nourishing yourself correctly. So, while the macronutrient ratio is important, so is figuring out your best macronutrient ratio in an intuitive way, rather than in an intellectual way!

There is one more principle that needs to be addressed, especially for those of you who do take nutritional supplements. And that brings us to principle number seven, which is:

7. Only take supplements that are right for your Nutritional Type. Avoid supplements that are wrong for your Nutritional Type.

While the right supplements for your Nutritional Type can definitely be helpful, they are not essential for most people to experience dramatic and even amazing health improvements. If you are on a tight budget, always prioritize spending your money on the best-quality food that is right for your Nutritional Type rather than spending it on supplements.

Raw Foods and Low-Temperature Cooking

The second NT principle is all about how you prepare your foods, so ideally you will want to eat them either raw or lightly cooked. Consuming foods in this form ensures that you get the maximum nutritional value from the foods, and the least amount of toxic byproducts.

You may not realize that cooking foods, particularly at high temperatures, actually creates health-harming compounds in the food, and this is something you definitely want to avoid. Eating foods as close to their natural form as possible is a primary goal with NT.

So, whenever possible you should seek out organic raw foods. This includes raw organic fruits and vegetables, organic raw dairy products like raw milk, raw kefir, and raw yogurt, and organic raw meats and seafood like steak tartar and salmon tartar, all according to your NT, of course.

However, raw dairy products can be very difficult to come by in the United States. If you cannot find a source of raw dairy products, you can substitute organic pasteurized dairy products, if they are agreeable to your body. Meanwhile, some people are opposed to eating raw meats and seafood. For this reason, it's acceptable to lightly cook your foods using low-temperature cooking.

Low-temperature cooking conserves more of the naturally occurring moisture and flavor in the food, plus, the food does not stick to the cookware. Most importantly, the food will be easier for your body to properly digest, and you will be conserving much more of the nutritional value of the food.

Low-Temperature Cooking Guidelines:

- Use a glass casserole dish with a cover. (The cover is very important.) The tighter the cover fits, the better. The size of the casserole dish should be appropriate for the amount of food being cooked. In other words, the casserole dish should be about the same size as what you are cooking, and should not be too big.

- Cook your food in the oven at 225 degrees Fahrenheit—*No Higher!*

- Allow for 12 to 15 minutes of cooking time per each 4 ounces of food being cooked, but decrease or increase the cooking time as needed.

Other healthy methods of cooking that are acceptable to use with NT include crock-pot cooking, poaching, steaming your food lightly, or searing your food on the outside (and leaving the inside very rare).

The Essential NT Guidelines: Protein Types

Protein Types can eat high-quality sources of protein and fat very freely, but they need to be very careful with their carbohydrate intake. It is very easy for a Protein Type to over-consume carbohydrates!

Contrary to the name, though, just because you are a Protein Type does not mean you need large amounts of protein. You may, in fact, need as little as 1 or 2 ounces of protein per meal depending on a variety of factors, including how much you weigh. But as little as one ounce of the right kind of protein could be enough to satisfy your body's need for protein—as long as you *eat it first and finish it completely* before you eat any other food.

Here are some tendencies and characteristics of Protein Types:

- They have strong appetites

- They tend to think about food a lot, even when they're not hungry

- They do not do well with fasting

- They do not feel well (especially mood-wise) if they skip a meal

- When they crave sugar or refined carbs, it will feel good to them in the moment if they eat some (but eating sugar or refined carbs will never satisfy a Protein Type's cravings for long)

- Eating sugar or refined carbs will typically stimulate their desire for more sugar or refined carbs

- They also have cravings for fatty, salty foods, and these foods have a more satisfying effect

- They will feel hungry most of the time if they eat a low-fat or vegetarian-type diet

No More Food Cravings, Plus Weight Loss!

Shirley is 63 years young and is a retired nurse. She has a long history of being overweight and having heart palpitations. As a new patient, she was about 100 pounds overweight and had failed on all of the diet programs she tried. She was simply unable to sustain any significant weight loss.

Shirley started having heart palpitations in 1988 while getting ready for her daughter's graduation. Eventually, she was given the effective but dangerous calcium channel blocker Verapamil, which she continues to take—although, she reports that she has not had heart palpitations for about 10 years.

In Nutritional Typing, she was assessed as a Protein Type. Her comprehensive blood test clearly indicated that she had been over-consuming carbohydrates, (Her insulin level was 10 and her leptin level was 29.4. Also, she was deficient in vitamin D (18)).

For three months, Shirley followed the prime Protein Type meal plan as faithfully as she could and she continues to feel much better. Specifically, her mood has dramatically improved, her energy is about 80 percent better, her mental clarity is sharper and it continues to improve.

The most remarkable aspect, though, is that she continues to be completely free of cravings for carbohydrates. After a meal, she can easily go for about six hours before she feels a need to eat again. Additionally, after some adjustments were made in her portions of protein, fat, and carbohydrates at every meal, she has lost 11 pounds—without dieting.

—*Shirley D, East Windsor, New Jersey*

The Prime Protein Type Meal Plan Guidelines

Protein Type foods typically have the following characteristics:

• Higher in total fat

• Lower in total carbohydrate

• Vegetable carbohydrates are relatively low in potassium and most green leafy vegetables are avoided

• Protein sources are high in purine amino acids, so dark red meats like beef, lamb, and dark poultry are preferable

The table for Protein Type foods is not easily displayed in this book format so it is freely available at my website: You will also find a link on that page that allows you to take the computerized nutritional typing test that can help you identify your nutritional type:

www.mercola.com/proteintype

Protein Types should follow the following guidelines with their meal plans for optimal health:

1. Choose *all* of your foods from the Protein Type food chart following these guidelines (except any foods that you are allergic, intolerant, or sensitive to).

2. Give faithful attention to food quality, eating fresh, organic food as often as possible and, ideally, only eating meats from healthy, humanely raised animals.

3. Follow our three-part Protein Type meal plan for your breakfast, lunch, and dinner. Each meal should be eaten in three separate parts (think in terms of a three-course meal). Parts one and two are *essential*, but part three is optional:

Part 1: Eat high-quality meat, fowl, fish, or seafood listed on the Protein Type food chart at *every* meal, and always eat a serving of meat, fowl, fish or seafood *first. Finish it completely* before you touch any carbohydrates!

(Remember, as little as 1 or 2 ounces of meat, fowl, fish, or seafood may be enough for you at any meal. However, feel free to eat the amount that feels right to you.)

Part 2: Consume some very low-carb or low-carb vegetable nutrition with every meal. Also, consume at least one of the following complementary foods along with your vegetable nutrition:

Raw Cream	Coconut
Raw Butter	Coconut Cream
Raw Cheese	Coconut Oil
Raw Cottage Cheese	Seeds
Avocado	Nuts
Olives	Nut Butters
Olive Oil	

Part 3: You may consume any of the following *in small amounts,* and only at the *very end of your meal* or not at all:

Artichoke Hearts	White Potato	Apple
Carrots	Winter Squash	Pear
Peas	Chestnuts	Banana
Beans	Raw Milk	Cranberries
Lentils	Raw Kefir	
Whole Grains	Raw Yogurt	

Do not eat any of these foods at the start of a meal or in between meals. Also, when eating Part 3 foods, always eat them with some additional high-quality fat or oil.

4. Focus on making the right food choices and eating in the right way. This means always eat your most metabolically important food first (Part 1) and eat the other foods at your meal in the right order (Parts 2 and 3). As for how much you should eat, initially let your appetite be your guide and learn from your experience. Listen to your body and trust what it tells you.

5. Eat consciously. Pay attention to what you are eating and if you do not already do so, then begin to practice eating slowly and chewing your food thoroughly.

6. If you need a snack in between meals, choose any of the foods from the Protein Type food chart that are printed in black. The foods from the chart that are printed in red should *never* be eaten as snacks in between meals.

7. To help yourself fall asleep and stay asleep, feel free to eat a Protein-Type-appropriate snack before going to bed (but be careful to not overeat).

Extreme Anxiety Relief (Protein Type)

Jon is a 44-year-old, highly successful entrepreneur who was running a half-billion-dollar company. He was referred to me by a close friend for an 11-year history of chronic anxiety that had failed to respond to some of the best psychotherapy in the country, including EFT.

Please understand that this anxiety was nearly debilitating and crippled him from leading a normal life. It was an enormous hardship for him to run his business with this type of handicap.

What made the issue even more interesting is that he had a phenomenally healthy lifestyle. Aside from being successful in business, he had also competed as a semi-professional athlete and was in excellent health. He clearly did not have an exercise deficiency.

He chose healthy foods but this turned out to be his achilles heel. Although they were healthy, biodynamic, organic foods, they were not correct for his metabolic type. In fact, they were the exact opposite of what his body required.

He was essentially eating a very healthy vegetarian, low-fat diet. Once we did his Nutritional Type and found out that he was a Protein Type, miracles occurred.

His anxiety rapidly resolved by over 90 percent until he went off his program and avoided the extra fat and protein that his body required.

Continued on page 25

Jon did find that eating a small amount of grain after eating some of his high purine meat and vegetables has worked to completely satisfy his appetite until his next meal. He still does experience a little bit of stress-related anxiety, but he no longer experiences anxiety attacks.

—Jon, St. Charles, IL

Optimal Meal Ideas for Protein Types

When you receive the food chart for your specific NT, you will be free to create meals using any of your recommended foods. Here we've compiled a few ideas to get you started.

- Have a rare rib eye steak or some steak tartar, finish this completely, and then have a spinach and mushroom omelet (and finish it completely). (If this seems like a lot of food, remember you can eat as little as 1 ounce of each.) Then, if desired, end this meal with some fresh apple slices slathered with raw almond butter* and topped off with walnuts. (*Mix some freshly ground flaxseed meal into the raw almond butter.)

- Have a seared flank steak, finish this completely, and then have an organic baby spinach salad with mushroom caps, avocado, olives, pistachio nuts, and pumpkin seeds. Top off the salad with some chopped chives and as much olive oil as desired. Finish the salad completely and then have one or two artichoke hearts with high-lignan flaxseed oil drizzled on top.

- Have some salmon tartar or smoked salmon (lox), finish this completely, and then have a salad made with organic baby spinach leaves, asparagus tips, and sliced mushroom caps (no stems) mixed with olive oil and fresh dill. Finish the salad completely and then have some Protein Type "Banana Cream Pudding" made by blending 1 raw egg, 1 or 2 heaping tablespoons of raw cream, and a small partly green banana.

- Have some sliced roast beef, finish this completely, and then have some Protein Type "Cole Slaw" (made with freshly grated cauliflower and raw cream, seasoned with salt and pepper).

Finish this completely and then have 4–6 ounces of yogurt mixed with some freshly ground flaxseed meal and chopped walnuts.

- Have one to three chicken legs (cold or hot), finish this completely, and then have some celery stalks dipped into organic peanut butter.* Finish this completely and then if desired, have a small serving of oatmeal with raw cream or raw butter, plus some chopped walnuts and cinnamon sprinkled on top. (*Mix some freshly ground flaxseed meal into the organic peanut butter.)

- Have some thinly sliced strips of raw salmon fillet with a small amount of salmon roe (caviar) on top of each slice of salmon fillet (or to keep it real simple have a can of sardines), finish this completely and then have some steamed asparagus with half of an avocado. Finish this completely and then end this meal with a serving of peas and carrots along with lots of raw butter.

- Have some ground beef, bison, or dark-meat turkey, finish this completely and then have some "mock mashed potatoes" (made with thoroughly steamed and then mashed cauliflower plus lots of raw butter). Finish the mock mashed potatoes completely, and then end this meal with Protein Type "Coconut-Banana Cream Pudding" (made by blending 1 raw egg, 1/4 cup of raw cream, 1/4 cup of fresh coconut meat chopped into small pieces, and a small partly green banana).

- Have a whole chicken leg (with the thigh), finish this completely and then have 3–4 ounces of fresh celery/spinach juice with 1–2 ounces of raw cream and 1 raw egg mixed into the juice. Finish this completely and then end this meal with some fresh organic corn on the cob along with lots of raw butter and a sprinkle of salt.

- Have some duck breast, finish this completely, and then have steamed asparagus, cauliflower, and string beans with lots of raw butter. Finish this completely and end this meal with a small pear that is sliced and slathered with raw almond butter.* (*Mix some freshly ground flaxseed meal into the raw almond butter.)

The Essential NT Guidelines: Carb Types

Carb Types can eat high-quality sources of carbohydrates very freely, but they need to be careful with their intake of protein—and they need to be even more careful with their intake of fat. It is very easy for a Carb Type to over-consume fat.

People who are Carb Types need a diet comprised of relatively small amounts of proteins and fat compared to carbs. Excess fat and protein will leave them feeling drained and sluggish or even hyper, wired, quick to anger, and irritable. It's important for Carb Types to eat low-fat (*but not non-fat*) foods.

They generally need to avoid red meats, with the exception of ostrich, and when they eat meat, it should be light-colored fish, the white meat of chicken or turkey, or all of the meat from a cornish hen, as these are low-purine proteins. Carb Types typically do well with grains, especially if they are not struggling with elevated insulin problems like extra weight, diabetes, high cholesterol, or high blood pressure, but grains are *not* their primary source of carbohydrates—vegetables are!

Here are the typical characteristics of a Carb Type:

- They have relatively light appetites
- They don't think about food much, unless they are hungry
- They have a high tolerance for carbs
- They can skip a meal if they have to, and it doesn't hurt their energy or mood
- They can enhance their feeling of well-being through fasting
- They typically don't like meat
- They typically don't like adding salt to their food
- They love salads
- They feel great after drinking fresh, organic vegetable juice
- They feel good after drinking freshly squeezed orange juice

The table for carb type foods is not easily displayed in this book format so it is freely available at my web site. You will also find a link on that page that allows you to take the computerized nutritional typing test that can help you identify which nutritional type you are.

www.mercola.com/carbtype

Diabetes Improves on HIGH-Carb Diet!

Paula is a 64-year-old diabetic and she has struggled with high triglycerides and very high cholesterol. Her comprehensive blood test clearly indicated insulin-resistant type 2 diabetes. Her previous physician enriched the drug companies by prescribing Lipitor, a drug that in no way, shape, or form treats the cause of the problem but gives Pfizer a cool $13 billion a year in revenues. Fortunately, she could not tolerate it. (She probably got a "thank you" note from her liver for stopping the Lipitor!)

Paula is five feet tall and was about 30 pounds overweight when she visited the Optimal Wellness Center in April of 2006. As a new patient, she expressed frustration that:

"No matter what I do, I just can't seem to lose weight and keep it off."

She also reported that she loves desserts. In fact, she has a history of having strong cravings for sugar and bread. (Cravings for sugar, bread, or other refined grain products are *always* a big clue that someone is not eating right for their type of metabolism.)

Through Nutritional Typing, Paula was identified as a strong Carb Type. Well, it took Paula some time to do the planning and preparation necessary before she could consistently eat right for her NT, but, in the middle of June 2006, she did begin to follow our prime Carb Type nutrition plan about 90 percent to 95 percent of the time.

Over the course of the next four to five months, Paula realized the following benefits:

- She experienced a huge reduction in her cravings for sugar and bread

- Her Carb Type meals were so satisfying to her, she could easily go for five to six hours after breakfast and lunch before she began to feel hungry again

Continued on page 29

- Her energy, stamina, mood, and mental clarity all improved

- She lost 18.25 pounds—Without Dieting!

All of these benefits really helped to improve the quality of Paula's daily life. From a blood chemistry perspective, the value of our Carb Type nutrition plan was shown in the dramatic improvements she realized from her first blood test in April, compared to her second blood test in September.

It is important to keep in mind that these improvements began to be achieved when Paula started to eat right for her NT and used food as her medicine! Also, keep in mind that she is 64 years of age and she had only been eating right for her NT for three months when her blood test was repeated.

Test results from April 28, 2006

- Insulin: 13
- Glucose: 144
- Triglycerides: 238
- Total Cholesterol: 298
- HDL's: 45
- LDL's: 205

Test results from September 21, 2006

- Insulin: 5
- Glucose: 85
- Triglycerides: 125
- Total Cholesterol: 259
- HDL's: 48
- LDL's: 186

She *did not* take any prescription drugs!

Paula's insulin and glucose levels from September are not only no longer at diabetic levels—these levels are outstandingly healthy for a Carb Type in her age group.

Her levels of triglycerides, total cholesterol, HDL's and LDL's still have lots of room for further improvement, but she is no longer at high risk for heart disease. In fact, every day that she eats right for her Nutritional Type she moves further away from disease and she gets closer and closer to realizing her full health potential at this time of her life.

—*Paula, Fruit Heights, Utah*

The Prime Carb Type Meal Plan Guidelines

When you receive your Carb Type food chart, you will know which foods are ideal for your type of metabolism. Here are the guidelines to follow to make each meal a movement toward excellent health:

1. Make a commitment to choose all of your foods from the Carb Type food chart following these guidelines (except any foods that you are allergic, intolerant, or sensitive to).

2. Eat fresh, organic food as often as possible and consider what you will eat raw and what you will eat cooked. When cooking, never overcook your food. Use low-temperature cooking as often as you can.

3. Drink three servings a day of fresh, organic, vegetable juice. Each serving of juice should be between 8 and 16 ounces.

4. Start every meal with some fresh, organic, *raw* vegetable or fruit nutrition. Drinking fresh, organic vegetable juice that includes a small amount of fruit is a great way for a Carb Type to start every meal.

5. At least two-thirds of the vegetable nutrition in each serving of juice should come from very-low-carb or low-carb vegetables (you can check your Carb Type food chart for vegetable classifications).

6. If you do not have fresh, organic, vegetable juice available to you then start your meal with 6 to 8 ounces of freshly squeezed orange juice, or simply eat some whole and raw, fresh, organic vegetable or fruit nutrition, such as a tomato, an orange, or an apple. Or, you could have a vegetable salad with lettuce, cherry tomatoes, bell pepper, and cucumber plus a small amount of fruit such as pineapple or kiwi.

7. Be sure to eat Carb Type proteins.

   Breakfast proteins include:

   • Cooked egg whites with just a small amount of cooked yolk

- A whole raw egg

- Low-fat yogurt, low-fat kefir, low-fat milk, or low-fat cottage cheese

- Whole grains (especially oats) may also have enough protein to satisfy a Carb Type's need for protein at breakfast

Lunch proteins include:

- Low-fat cheese, low-fat cottage cheese, low-fat yogurt, low-fat kefir, low-fat milk

- A whole raw egg

- One whole cooked egg plus two or three additional cooked egg whites

- Light-colored fish, chicken breast, or turkey breast

Dinner proteins include:

- Cornish hen, chicken breast, turkey breast, light-colored fish, or ostrich

- A whole raw egg

- One whole cooked egg plus two or three additional cooked egg whites

- Low-fat cheese, low-fat cottage cheese, low-fat yogurt, low-fat kefir, or low-fat milk

8. Eat two salads a day, one with lunch and one with dinner.

9. If you need a snack in between meals, choose any of the vegetables or fruits from the Carb Type food chart that are printed in black. The foods that are printed in red should not be eaten as snacks in between meals. Low-fat dairy products may also be included with your snack foods.

10. Focus on making the right food choices and eating in the right way. This means always eat your most metabolically important foods first, which for Carb Types are fresh, organic, raw vegetables and fruits. Also, eat consciously. Pay attention to what you are eating and if you do not already do so, then begin to practice

eating slowly and chewing your food thoroughly. Initially, let your appetite be your guide when deciding how much to eat. Listen to your body and trust what it tells you.

Blood Pressure Improves Dramatically

The story below is from someone who had struggled with very high blood pressure for some time. She had applied the Atkins-type, low-carb, high-protein diet for her blood pressure challenge and it failed miserably. She was even eating organic foods!

Why did it fail? Because, she was a Carb Type. If she were a protein type, she would have had phenomenal results, just like many of the successful Atkins proponents.

Fortunately, she was a subscriber to our site and had taken our online NT test that provided her with the correct diet recommendations for her and, as you can see by her story below, it worked like an absolute charm.

Mieltje is a 54-year-old woman who had her thyroid removed in 1984. She gained quite a bit of weight over the years and also had high blood pressure. She had always been able to control high blood pressure with magnesium, but lately that had not worked.

Here is her story:

"After 10 days of the NT diet, my blood pressure has dropped 40 points. I was getting readings of 200/160, and yesterday I had 123 over 73. Still spikes, but is dropping steadily.

Unbelievable. I never believed I was a carb person, and have been avoiding them for years, still gaining weight. Steady increase in blood pressure, despite eating healthy, organic foods.

And who would have thought the order in which you eat them matters. I always craved bread and potatoes more than dessert. I'm in heaven finishing a meal with a red potato, or following egg for breakfast with flax wheat toast. And the fog is clearing. Still waiting to see a weight drop, but the blood pressure change is amazing!"

—Mieltje, Deer Park, IL

Optimal Meal Ideas for Carb Types

Carb Types can use these ideal meal suggestions to get started.

- For breakfast, start with a fresh vegetable juice, then have an egg white and vegetable omelet, or a cup of freshly cooked oatmeal or other whole grain, topped off with fresh apple slices and cinnamon. As an option, you can add in a raw egg white while the cereal is still hot (the heat from the cereal will be enough to properly cook the egg white).

- Have a Carb Type breakfast shake made by blending 4-6 ounces of reduced-fat milk or plain low-fat yogurt, 1/2 cup to 1 cup of fresh fruit, 1 whole raw egg, and 1 teaspoon of unheated, raw honey.

- For lunch, start with another fresh vegetable juice, then have a salad with some low-fat cheese or cottage cheese and a dressing made with low-fat plain yogurt as your source of protein (flavor the plain yogurt with fresh chives or fresh dill).

- For lunch, start with a fresh vegetable juice, then have a sandwich made with sliced turkey or chicken breast with lettuce, tomato, onion, and mustard on slices of whole sprouted-grain or sourdough bread. If desired, have some fresh, organic corn on the cob to finish your meal.

- For dinner, start with another fresh vegetable juice, then have another salad with some chicken breast, turkey breast, Cornish hen, light-colored fish, or ostrich as your source of protein, or have a serving of Carb Type chicken vegetable soup. If desired, finish this meal with a slice of whole sprouted-grain or sourdough bread, or a small baked potato with a small amount of olive oil or butter.

Prime Carb Type Juicing Recipes

- Each serving size of juice should be between 8 and 16 ounces

- At least two-thirds of every juice should be made with very-low-carb or low carb vegetables, or both (see the Carb Type food chart for vegetable classification).

1. Cucumber, tomato, and zucchini with some lemon and lime

2. Cucumber, romaine lettuce, and zucchini with some lemon and lime

3. Cucumber, romaine lettuce, a whole beet (with the stems and leaves), plus some carrot and apple

4. Cucumber, red and green leaf lettuce, parsley, and a kiwi

5. Cucumber, romaine lettuce, parsley, and pineapple

6. Cherry tomatoes, bell pepper, parsley, and lime

7. Green cabbage, green leaf lettuce, carrot, and apple

8. Cucumber, romaine lettuce, carrot, and apple

9. Tomato, bell pepper, parsley, kale, carrot, and apple

10. Red or green cabbage, broccoli (the stem, not the tops), carrot, and apple

11. Romaine lettuce, fennel, carrot, ginger root, and fresh mint leaves

12. Tomato, bell pepper, parsley, kale, garlic, ginger root, lemon, and lime. (This is the "protection recipe" and it is especially good for strengthening immune system activity.)

In cold weather, feel free to add some fresh ginger root to every juice recipe. Ginger root is well known to be a "warming" herb.

The Essential NT Guidelines: Mixed Types

If you are a Mixed Type, you have lots of good news. If you are this type, you have the broadest selection of food available to you. Your primary concern will be to make sure you appropriately combine your protein and carb food types.

Traditional metabolic typing does not appreciate this and this was one of the largest frustrations we had with it. Mixed Types in the old system simply did not seem to do as well as Protein or Carb Types.

However, after a few years of working with the Metabolic Typing, we realized this relative lack of response was largely related to improper combination of their protein and carb type foods. Once we incorporated this simple change, we noticed the same type of radical improvements for mixed type individuals as protein and carb types.

Mixed types have very broad nutritional needs. They need foods that are right for both Protein Types and Carb Types. They typically gravitate toward eating a large variety of foods, and eating a large variety of foods is most important for a Mixed Type. Mixed Types can eat high-quality sources of protein and fat together with very low-carb or low-carb vegetables very freely, but they need to be careful with their intake of high-carb foods.

Mixed Types can identify with many of the characteristics that both Protein Types and Carb Types are familiar with, but Mixed Types do not experience these characteristics as intensely as Protein Types or Carb Types. They feel very good with, and thus gravitate toward, eating meat and vegetable type meals such as a salad with meat or fish, chicken and vegetable soup, or beef stew.

The classic "balanced" meal that is so commonly advocated for everyone actually works best for Mixed Types. The table for mixed type foods is not easily displayed in this book format so it is freely available at my website. You will also find a link on that page that allows you to take the computerized nutritional typing test that can help you identify which nutritional type you are:

www.mercola.com/mixedtype

Hypothyroid and High Blood Pressure Improves

Lou had a history of high blood pressure and low thyroid function. He developed hypertension about five years ago, and he was shown to have a thyroid problem a year earlier.

He has been on Synthroid since August 2005, which was able to reduce his fatigue and brain fog.

He exercises religiously and has competed in two Iron Man competitions. His initial NT assessment in November 2005 found him to be a Carb Type. For over 10 weeks he faithfully followed the prime Carb Type meal plan and he experienced significant improvement in his energy and stamina.

Continued on page 36

Additionally, he had no cravings and was able to go four to six hours in between meals before he felt the need to eat again. However, he eventually began to feel a need to increase his intake of raw butter and felt less satisfied with his Carb Type meals. He tried some raw red meat, which he enjoyed and found to be very satisfying.

Around the same time, he increased the frequency, intensity and duration of his exercise and stopped taking his medication for hypertension. Amazingly, his thyroid disease remarkably improved. In February 2006, Lou repeated his NT assessment and in his second report, he was re-assessed as a protein type.

At this point, it was clear that Lou was initially only a functional Carb Type and now he may only be a functional Protein Type. Time will tell, but it is likely that he is a Mixed Type. At this time, Lou continues to feel very good eating an almost all raw food version of the prime Protein Type meal plan. His energy is good and his blood pressure has been in a healthier range. He recently completed a half Iron Man competition and felt very strong doing so.

—*Lou, Santa Barbara, California*

The Prime Mixed Type Meal Plan Guidelines

Mixed Types should follow these guidelines to achieve optimal health.

1. Make a commitment to choose *all* of your foods from the Mixed Type primary and secondary food charts following these guidelines. Mixed Types should eat foods that are right for both Protein Types and Carb Types at every meal.

2. Give faithful attention to food quality. Eat fresh, organic food as often as possible and consider what you will eat raw and what you will eat cooked. When cooking, never overcook your food. Use low temperature cooking as often as you can, and, ideally, only eat meats from healthy, humanely raised animals.

3. The prime Mixed Type meal plan is based on starting *every meal* with high-quality proteins and fat together with vegetable nutrition selected from the Primary Foods Chart. These foods are printed in green, blue, and brown, and they are your most metabolically important foods. Always consume your most metabolically important foods *first at every meal.*

4. From the food choices available on the Mixed Type Primary Foods Chart, create the foundation for each one of your meals with faithful attention to the following Mixed Type food-combining guidelines:

    • Proteins printed in green (Protein Type protein) should be eaten with vegetables printed in green, which are Carb Type vegetables.

    • Proteins printed in blue (Carb Type protein) should be eaten with vegetables printed in blue (Protein Type vegetables).

    • Eating a protein that is printed in green plus a protein that is printed in blue, together with at least one vegetable printed in green and at least one vegetable printed in blue, *and* some additional high-quality fat or oil printed in brown, is the *Mixed Type meal ideal.*

5. Focus on implementing the Mixed Type meal ideal as often as you can and eat consciously! Pay attention to what you are eating and if you do not already doing so, then begin to practice eating slowly and chewing your food thoroughly. As for how much protein, how many vegetables, and how much additional fat or oil you should eat initially, let your appetite be your guide. Listen to your body, trust what it tells you, and learn from your experience!

6. When eating breakfast, lunch and dinner, any of the foods on the Secondary Foods Chart may be eaten—but only after you have completely finished your Primary Foods.

7. If you need a snack in between meals, choose your snack from the Primary Foods Chart or from the nuts and seeds that are on the Secondary Foods Chart. (This includes nut butters such as almond

butter and seed butters such as tahini.) The foods printed in both orange and red on the Secondary Foods Chart, including the sweet fruits, are not appropriate for between-meal snacks.

Rare Childhood Disease Improves Dramatically

Krista was 4 years old when she visited our clinic and had been diagnosed with Angelman's Syndrome, which is a relatively rare disease. Children with this have a stiff, jerky gait, absent speech, excessive laughter, and seizures. Krista also had irregular heartbeats.

It is common for conventional medicine to develop very precise diagnostic criteria for relatively exotic symptom combinations that result from not following natural medical approaches. They have no clue what to attribute the cause to and are equally clueless about solutions. About the only solace they provide to patients with these conditions is a worthless label.

Krista's Mom, Karen, began feeding her a gluten/casein-free diet and she immediately slept better, her diaper rash cleared up, her cognitive function improved, and her staring spells diminished.

However, Krista continued to experience a number of other physical and behavioral symptoms that indicated severe underlying metabolic imbalance. Her NT test showed that she was a Protein Type.

Krista continued to engage in aggressive behavior (kicking, biting, slapping, pulling hair) until it was discovered that she was intolerant to any food that comes from a cow—even raw dairy. Avoiding all cow-derived foods helped to improve Krista's behavior.

Also, Karen has been feeding Krista raw bison, raw salmon, and raw eggs, and she reports that overall Krista's progress has been "fabulous." She has seen amazing improvement in Krista's cognitive and learning abilities.

Krista has been talking, which was amazing in light of the fact that doctors had previously told Karen that Krista would never be able to talk. She also has more awareness, seeks to be more involved in activities, and has learned to ride a bike. She no longer has constipation and eczema. Additionally, she is no longer intolerant to beef.

This is an absolute amazing testimony to the power of natural foods that are right for a child's Nutritional Type. Application of very simple approaches has resulted in dramatic improvements in a condition that is generally regarded as hopeless in conventional medicine.

—*Krista, Mount Pleasant, Michigan*

Optimal Meal Ideas for Mixed Types

Here are some examples of prime meals for Mixed Types:

Breakfast:

- If you have a light appetite, have 8 ounces of fresh vegetable juice made with celery and spinach or asparagus, mixed together with 1 raw egg and 1 or 2 tablespoons of raw cream. Or, have some cottage cheese mixed with grated cauliflower or with chopped celery and spinach, mixed together with high-lignan flaxseed oil.

- If you have a stronger appetite for breakfast, have a chicken or turkey salad made with both the white and dark meat, together with a mix of chopped celery, tomato, parsley, scallion, and one or two tablespoons of olive oil or raw cream (instead of mayonnaise). Serve this on a bed of romaine lettuce.

- If desired, either of the above breakfasts can be finished with an apple or pear slathered with raw almond butter or simply have some fresh fruit by itself.

Lunch:

- Mix together sliced roast beef and grated raw cheese with chopped bell pepper, mushroom, onion, and olive oil.

- Have sliced salmon or salmon tartar with a lettuce salad that includes cherry tomatoes, cucumber, and avocado. Drizzle olive oil on top if desired.

- Wrap slices of turkey breast or ham around celery stalks and then dip into raw sour cream or fresh cream. (Mix some fresh herbs, such as chives or dill, into the cream.)

- Have some steak tartar or a rare and juicy burger on a bed of lettuce, tomato, and onion (without the bun, of course).

- If desired, any of the above lunches can be finished with a small serving of fresh fruit mixed into a small serving of raw kefir or raw yogurt.

Dinner:

- Start with a small baby, organic spinach salad that includes asparagus tips, sliced mushroom caps, fresh dill, olive oil, and the cheese of your choice. Then, choose any one of the following Mixed Type meal ideas for your main course:

    o Have steak tartar or a rare and juicy steak plus an egg, together with chopped bell pepper, mushrooms, onions, and olive oil.

    o Have a chicken thigh with some sablefish or tilapia together with steamed broccoli, kale, leek, and cauliflower. Put some raw butter on the vegetables.

- Familiar food combinations such as chicken vegetable soup or turkey vegetable soup (without noodles), beef stew or lamb stew (without carrots and potatoes), and chili (without the beans) are all recommended for Mixed Types not only at dinner, but *for any meal*.

- If desired, finish any of the above dinners with an "after dinner cocktail" of 6-8 ounces of fresh, organic vegetable juice. Or, if you feel a need for some starchy carbohydrates, have a small serving of wild rice eaten with walnuts and high-lignan flaxseed oil or a baked potato with raw butter.

Keeping Track of Your Body's Responses to Your New Meal Plan

When you first start eating right for your Nutritional Type, you'll want to pay careful attention to how your body is responding to the foods you're eating. This will eventually become second nature to you, but in the beginning we recommend using the tool that we have developed called: "Learning to Listen to Your Body."

This is a systematic and simple way to assess your response to your nutrition plan. Similar to a diary, the "Learning to Listen to your Body" sheets will help you learn from your experience and discover for yourself what is right for you.

And, remember, once you learn the guidelines that are right for you, and experience how your body feels, you'll find that NT is an

incredibly healthy way to eat for the rest of your life that, importantly, is not difficult and doesn't require burdensome effort.

Can Your Nutritional Type Change?

Your type can, in fact, change over time. However, for most people, once your Nutritional Type is correctly identified, it does not
change.

As far as your NT changing, this is a matter of the difference
between what we refer to as your "genetic type," or the NT that you
were born with, and your "functional type"—the NT that you are
simply functioning at today.

Occasionally your genetic type can weaken, and as a result, you
can move into a different NT pattern. This may be caused by:

- Eating the wrong foods for your Nutritional Type

- Stress

- Environmental factors such as seasonal changes

If this occurs after you start balancing your body chemistry, it is
possible that you will move back and forth between your genetic and
functional types. Until the strength is restored in your body, you may
therefore, move into different Nutritional Types.

However, if your genetic type is the same as your functional type
(and this is the case with most people), then your NT will most likely never change.

Either way, a change in your NT is not something you need to
worry about. You simply follow your program and retest occasionally to check on your Nutritional Type and see how you're doing.
When you follow your NT, things just work out in a very natural way.

What if I'm a Vegetarian and a Protein Type?

People who follow a vegetarian diet are often concerned about
changing their eating habits if they turn out to be Protein Types.
Unfortunately, some of the most seriously ill patients I have seen are
people who are Protein Types clinging to the belief that they need to
be a vegetarian. They are relying on their brain to help them select
foods rather than listening to the powerful intuitive clues their body

is providing them in essential feedback loops to help them improve their health.

This is because Protein Types need to eat high-purine animal protein in order to achieve optimal health. The whole point of NT is to identify what foods are right for your specific and unique biochemistry, and that goes far beyond any theory or belief. NT has to do with what is right for your genes, and what is right from a genetic standpoint in terms of the kinds of foods and kinds of nutrients that are right for your metabolism.

While being vegetarian might be a choice that benefits some people, it is a choice that is *not* conducive to health for Protein Types. People in this group tend to suffer terribly by developing numerous health problems and never achieving the level of health they are seeking if they choose to remain on a vegetarian diet.

I'm Having Problems With Digestion . . . What Do I Do?

To benefit from eating the right foods for your Nutritional Type, you must be able to digest your food properly. Your body, however, may be damaged and not able to produce the hydrochloric acid and enzymes necessary to properly digest your food.

If you are eating the foods that are right for your Nutritional Type, yet are having digestive problems such as:

- Belching or burping

- Food seeming like it's sitting like a rock in your stomach and just not moving through

- Your digestion seems unusually slow

- You have heartburn or intestinal gas

- Any other signs of indigestion

Remember to *eat consciously*! Pay attention to what you are eating and if you do not already do so, begin to practice eating slowly and chewing your food thoroughly.

It is also important to eat your food under calm conditions. You shouldn't be watching upsetting news on TV, having an argument with someone, or worrying about a problem you're dealing with while you eat. This is because stressful situations such as these will shut off the digestive process and make it much more difficult for you to digest your food.

You may also benefit from taking some hydrochloric acid or enzyme supplements with your meals to help your digestive process.

Taking a daily probiotic is also recommended. When taking supplements, you should seek an experienced natural medical clinician to guide you through the process.

Why Taking Supplements Can be Dangerous if you Don't Know Your NT

I'm very much opposed to the indiscriminate use of supplements, as they can cause far more harm than good. Foods can be wonderful for you if they are right for your Nutritional Type, but the challenging point for many to accept is that even locally biodynamically grown organic vegetables can be bad for you if they're wrong for your Nutritional Type. And when you apply that notion to a disease process, such as heart disease or high cholesterol, if you eat the wrong foods for your Nutritional Type you may increase your heart disease or bad cholesterol, even if those foods don't contain cholesterol.

Foods are good or bad for you, depending upon what's right for your Nutritional Type, and the identical scenario is also true for supplements. Vitamins and minerals have specific effects on your metabolism, so to simply start taking supplements because you read about them in an article or you hear friends say that it was good for them, is actually an unwise and potentially unhealthy thing to do. We do not recommend doing that.

Taking an individual nutrient or multivitamin that is wrong for your NT can cause or worsen an imbalance in your biochemistry.

When Will I Experience the Benefits of Nutritional Typing?

Most people will start to notice benefits of eating the right foods for their NT within the first few weeks. However, it is important to appreciate that you will continue to realize your full health potential over time.

If you are suffering from a degenerative process, you should give yourself a few years of really being faithful to the program. At the end of that time, when you look back you'll be amazed at the changes that have taken place in your body, just by eating the right foods—and stopping the wrong ones—for your Nutritional Type.

How Do I Find Out My Nutritional Type?

All of our patients at the Optimal Wellness Center (my health clinic just outside of Chicago) were required to take the computerized Metabolic Typing analysis as part of their evaluation in our clinic. The cost for that analysis, with a one-hour follow-up consultation with a therapist, was $180 (this was typically reimbursed by third-party insurance companies).

However, the high price of the analysis has prevented many people from taking this valuable test, which we believe should be available to everyone. A significant portion of that fee went to pay for the actual computerized test that was developed by Bill Wolcott.

To provide a less-expensive alternative, we've invested tens of thousands of dollars to develop a simpler, much more affordable test to nutritionally type you, and an online evaluation and support forum, which is moderated by one of the nutritionists that works in our clinic.

So, we now can finally offer the test to our online subscribers. All you need to do is go to:

www.mercola.com/nt

The cost of the test also includes participation for one month in our online forum so you can access the thousands of questions that people have already written and also have a full month of free one-on-one coaching with our Nutritional Typing coaches.

We are extremely excited to be able to offer the NT program, as those who apply its principles experience phenomenal health benefits. Give it a try for yourself, and experience for the first time what truly optimal health really feels like.

Chapter Two

Recipes

for Your

Nutritional Type

Salads

Arugula, Asparagus, and Olive Salad with Toasted Pine Nuts

4 servings

- 3 bunches arugula (CT), or spinach (PT)
- 2½ cups asparagus, trimmed and cut into 1–inch pieces
- 1 cup kalamata olives (or any other Greek olive)
- ½ cup toasted pine nuts

Dressing:

- ½ cup olive oil
- 2 cloves garlic, pressed
- 1 teaspoon red pepper flakes
- 2 tablespoons fresh cilantro, chopped
- Juice of 1 lemon

1. Quickly blanch asparagus and set aside.

2. Deseed the olives by cutting down the center lengthwise.

3. Combine the arugula, asparagus, and olives in a bowl.

4. Roast the pine nuts in a shallow pan at 325°F until brown.

5. Whisk the dressing together, pour over salad, and top with pine nuts.

Recipe Type	Calories	Total Fat (grams)	Carbs (grams)	Protein (grams)
Mixed	333	34	8	4
Carb	318	33	5	3
Protein	323	33	6	4

Black Bean, Sun-dried Tomato and White Fish Salad

4 servings

Salad:

- 1½ pounds white fish (any type) skinned and deboned (CT), or salmon (PT)
- 1 tablespoon coconut oil
  Salt and pepper, to taste
- ½ cup cooked quinoa
- ½ cup canned black beans (PT), or reduce to 1/4 cup (CT)
- 3 medium tomatillos
- 1 orange pepper, chopped
- 2 cups watercress (CT), or spinach (PT)

Vinaigrette:

- 1 chipotle chili
- 1 tablespoon fresh lemon juice
- 1 tablespoon champagne vinegar
- 1 tablespoon sun-dried tomatoes
- ½ teaspoon ground cumin
- ¼ teaspoon ground coriander
- 1 tablespoon cilantro, chopped
- ¼ cup flax seed oil
  Salt and pepper

1. Preheat oven to 350°F. Season the fish with salt and pepper, place in an oven safe pan with 1 tablespoon coconut oil, bake for 25–35 minutes.

2. Place one cup of quinoa in a pan with two cups water. Bring to boil and simmer for 15 minutes covered. When all the water is gone the quinoa is cooked. Use half a cup and save the rest for another quinoa recipe. *Continued on page 51*

Healthy Recipes for Your Nutritional Type

3. Mix together the black beans and quinoa, set aside. Blend all ingredients for vinaigrette in a food processor until well combined.

4. Mix together the white fish, tomatillos, orange pepper and watercress or spinach.

5. Then add the black beans and quinoa.

6. Pour vinaigrette over mixed vegetables and fish.

Recipe Type	Calories	Total Fat (grams)	Carbs (grams)	Protein (grams)
Mixed	505	17	40	50
Carb	413	10	32	49
Protein	599	24	48	50

Beef And Cucumber Salad

4 servings

Salad:

- 1 pound lean rare roast beef, thinly sliced
- 2 cups English cucumber, thinly sliced
- 1 small red onion, thinly sliced
- ¼ cup parsley, chopped
- 3 tablespoons capers
- ½ tomato, thinly sliced
- Lettuce for garnish

Dressing:

- ½ lemon, juiced
- 1 clove garlic, minced
- ½ teaspoon salt
- 1 teaspoon sugar
- ½ teaspoon ginger powder
- 2 teaspoons Dijon mustard
- ¼ cup olive oil

1. Dressing: Add all dressing ingredients to a bowl except for the oil. Gradually whisk in oil. Makes 1/3 cup.

2. Combine salad ingredients. Cover and refrigerate for 1–3 hours.

3. Put a lettuce leaf on each plate and top with a serving of the salad.

Cooking Tips:

PT: May decrease cucumber to 1 cup if desired.

CT: Use 1/2 pound roast beef or use slivered turkey breast.

Recipe Type	Calories	Total Fat (grams)	Carbs (grams)	Protein (grams)
Mixed	347	22	7	30
Carb	268	19	7	20
Protein	343	22	6	30

Brown Rice and Fresh Veggies

6 servings

- 2 cups water
- ¼ teaspoon salt
- 1 cup brown rice
- 1 cup fresh grapes, cut in halves (CT), or pears, chopped (PT)
- ½ cup red pepper, chopped (CT), or asparagus, sliced (PT)
- 2 celery ribs, chopped
- ½ cup cucumber, chopped
- ¼ cup red onions, chopped finely
- 1 tablespoon chives, chopped
- 1 tablespoon olive oil
- 3 tablespoons lemon juice
- 2 tablespoons apple cider vinegar

1. Bring water to boil with salt. Add brown rice and briefly return to a boil, then reduce the heat and cover pot, simmer for 40–45 minutes. Set aside. Allow to cool at room temperature.

2. Combine grapes, bell pepper, celery, red onion, oil and lemon juice or vinegar. Stir in brown rice and serve.

Recipe Type	Calories	Total Fat (grams)	Carbs (grams)	Protein (grams)
Mixed	161	3	31	3
Carb	85	3	15	1
Protein	82	3	14	1

Chicken Salad With Herbs

4 servings

- 2 pounds boneless chicken
- 2 tablespoons olive oil
- 1 tablespoon coconut oil
- 2 tablespoons fresh tarragon, chopped
- 2 tablespoons fresh mint, chopped
- 2 tablespoons fresh rosemary, chopped
- 2 tablespoons fresh oregano, chopped
- 2 tablespoons fresh chives, chopped
- 2 tablespoons fresh cilantro, chopped
- 1 red bell pepper, deseeded and chopped
- 2 cucumbers, chopped (CT), or 8 oz. mushrooms, sliced (PT)
- 2 small oranges, peeled and sliced (CT), or green apple (PT)
- 1 red onion, chopped
- 4-6 cups fresh salad greens (CT), or spinach (PT)
- ½ cup toasted almonds or sesame seeds

Dressing:
- ½ cup sherry wine
- 1 tablespoon Dijon mustard
- 1 teaspoon kosher salt
- 2 shallots, finely chopped
- ½ cup extra virgin olive oil
- ¼ teaspoon freshly ground black pepper

1. In a medium saucepan, over medium heat, add the olive oil and coconut oil. Add the chicken breasts to the heated oil. Cook the chicken on both sides, until brown. About 10 minutes per side. *Continued on page 55*

2. Remove from pan and set aside to cool.

3. Meanwhile, mix the dressing ingredients in a covered jar and shake.

4. Slice the cooled chicken lengthwise into strips.

5. In a large bowl, combine the herbs, veggies, and salad greens. Toss gently. Add the chicken strips and dressing. Toss gently.

6. Top with toasted almonds and sesame seeds. Serve immediately.

CT: Eat only the white meat (breast).

PT: Eat only the dark meat (legs and thighs).

Recipe Type	Calories	Total Fat (grams)	Carbs (grams)	Protein (grams)
Mixed	646	49	22	32
Carb	655	49	24	32
Protein	639	49	21	32

Cabbage Crunch

6 servings

- ½ head red cabbage, chopped finely
- ½ head white cabbage, chopped finely
- ½ red onion, chopped
- ½ cup chopped cilantro
- ½ jalapeno pepper, minced (optional)

Dressing:

- 1 teaspoon gomasio (ground sesame with salt)
- 1 cup almond butter
- ½ cup cilantro, chopped
- 1 tablespoon toasted sesame oil
- 1 tablespoon minced fresh ginger
- ½ jalapeno pepper, chopped (optional)
- ½ lemon, juiced
- 1 tablespoon apple cider vinegar
- 1 tablespoon seasoned rice vinegar
- 1 cup olive oil
- 1 tablespoon white miso paste* (optional)

1. Mix the cabbage with the chopped onions. Add cilantro and jalapeno.

2. Place all the dressing ingredients into a food processor and blend briefly. Mix into salad mix and serve.

Recipe Type	Calories	Total Fat (grams)	Carbs (grams)	Protein (grams)
Mixed	671	63	26	10

Crisp and Crunchy Green Salad

4 servings

Salad:

- 1 head butter lettuce
- 1 whole avocado, chopped into chunks
- 1 cup sunflower seed sprouts
- 1 medium tomato, chopped into small pieces
- 1 medium cucumber
- ¼ cup toasted pine nuts

Dressing:

- ¼ cup olive oil
- ⅛ cup balsamic vinegar
- 1 clove garlic, crushed
- 1 teaspoon Dijon mustard

1. Rip or cut up the lettuce leaves and place in big bowl.

2. Cut up remaining vegetables and place in the bowl with lettuce

3. Toast pine nuts in an un-oiled skillet on medium heat for 4–5 minutes until lightly browned.

4. Whisk together the olive oil and vinegar, then add the crushed garlic, pour over salad and serve immediately.

Recipe Type	Calories	Total Fat (grams)	Carbs (grams)	Protein (grams)
Mixed	370	34	16	8

Dandelion and Fennel Salad

4 servings

Salad:

     1   bunch dandelion greens, cut very finely

     ½   bulb fennel, thinly sliced

     2   cups napa cabbage, sliced thinly

     ½   cup bean sprouts

Dressing:

     1   lemon juiced

     1   tablespoon mirin*

     ⅛   teaspoon sesame oil

     1   teaspoon apple cider vinegar

     1   teaspoon tamari soy sauce

     2   tablespoons olive oil

     ¼   teaspoon maple syrup

1. Place the dandelion greens, napa cabbage, fennel, and bean sprouts in large bowl.

2. Mix all the ingredients for the dressing together and dress the salad.

Can be found in the Asian aisle at the grocery store, or at an Asian market.

Recipe Type	Calories	Total Fat (grams)	Carbs (grams)	Protein (grams)
Mixed	197	17	13	3
Carb	209	17	16	3
Protein	218	17	17	5

French Bean Salad

4 servings

Salad:

  1 pound French beans, ends removed (PT), or zucchini, sliced (CT)

  4 medium green onions, finely sliced

  2 tomatoes, chopped

  4 tablespoons walnuts, chopped

Dressing:

  1 clove garlic, crushed

  2 tablespoons apple cider vinegar

  1 teaspoon Dijon mustard

  1 teaspoon raw honey

  ½ cup olive oil

1. Blanch the beans by putting beans into a pan of boiling water and cooking for about 3 minutes. Immediately transfer to a bowl of ice water, allow the beans to cool. Remove, drain, and place in a bowl.

2. Place the beans in a large bowl and add the green onions, tomatoes, and walnuts.

3. In a small bowl whisk all the ingredients for the dressing. Pour over the salad

Recipe Type	Calories	Total Fat (grams)	Carbs (grams)	Protein (grams)
Mixed	724	34	73	22
Carb	336	32	12	4
Protein	633	34	67	20

Dandelion Greens with Celeriac and Tangerine

4 servings

Salad:

1 bunch dandelion greens, chopped (CT), or spinach (PT)

1 medium lime, juiced

⅛ teaspoon sea salt

1 medium celeriac, shredded

10 medium basil leaves, chopped finely

1 medium tangerine, sliced

¼ cup pine nuts, toasted

Dressing:

1 medium tangerine, juiced

3 tablespoons olive oil

1 tablespoon lime juice

½ teaspoon tangerine zest

1 teaspoon maple syrup (optional)

1. Wash and chop the dandelion leaves in 1/2 inch pieces and discard tough ends.

2. Pour lime juice into the chopped leaves and add the salt.

3. Massage the dandelion leaves with the lime juice and salt for up to 3 minutes or until the leaves are wilted.

4. Add the shredded celeriac, basil leaves and tangerine. Add the toasted pine nuts and mix everything together.

Continued on page 61

5. Use a grater or microplane to zest the tangerine, whisk together all ingredients for dressing and pour over the salad (if you are using later save the dressing until you are going to eat the salad otherwise it will ruin the salad.)

6. Garnish with extra tangerine slices and serve.

Recipe Type	Calories	Total Fat (grams)	Carbs (grams)	Protein (grams)
Mixed	197	16	13	3
Carb	209	17	16	3
Protein	218	17	17	5

Gobble Up Your Greens And Peas

4 servings

- 1 package of nitrate-free, dark turkey strips
- 2 tablespoons olive oil
- 1 tablespoon coconut oil
- 3 large bundles of collard greens, chopped (CT), or spinach (PT)
- 2 cups canned black-eyed peas
- 1 medium onion, chopped
- 2 cloves of garlic, minced (CT), or 1 clove garlic (PT)

1. In a medium saucepan, over medium heat, add 1 tablespoon olive oil and coconut oil. Add the turkey strips, cook for 3–5 minutes. Turn to cook evenly.

2. Reduce heat to low, remove turkey strips from the pan, and cover with a paper towel. Set aside.

3. In the same pan, over medium heat, add the remaining olive oil. When oil is hot, add the onion and garlic, sauté for about 2 minutes.

4. Add the canned beans; stir into the onion and garlic mixture.

5. Add about half of the collard greens to the pan. Lower heat, cover and let steam for about 1 minute. Add the other half of the greens, water to moisten, cover and steam again until all greens are steamed.

Continued on page 63

6. While greens are steaming, cut turkey strips into 1-inch pieces. Stir in the strips to the bean and greens mixture to warm again.

7. Divide equal amounts of mixture to a plate and garnish with parsley.

Recipe Type	Calories	Total Fat (grams)	Carbs (grams)	Protein (grams)
Mixed	504	14	72	32
Carb	508	14	73	29
Protein	503	15	68	32

Grapefruit and Arugula Salad with Avocado

4 servings

- 5 ounces baby arugula (CT), or 5 ounces spinach (PT)
- 2 grapefruits, peeled and sectioned (CT), or 1 grapefruit (PT)
- 1 avocado, sliced

Dressing:
- 2 tablespoons white wine vinegar
- 1 tablespoon grapefruit juice
- 1 tablespoon grated fresh ginger
- 1 teaspoon grated grapefruit zest
- ½ teaspoon sea salt
- ¼ cup extra virgin olive oil
- Freshly ground black pepper

1. Grate 1 teaspoon of zest from the grapefruit, reserving for the salad dressing. Peel the grapefruits by cutting off each end then working your knife around the perimeter. This method removes the membrane from all outside edges. Hold the peeled grapefruit in one hand over a bowl. Use a paring knife and in a sawing motion cut each segment from the membrane on both sides. Let the juice drip into the bowl and place segments in another bowl. When all segments have been removed from both grapefruit squeeze the remaining juice from the membranes and reserve 1 tablespoon of the juice for the dressing.

Continued on page 65

2. To prepare the dressing, combine all ingredients except the oil in a bowl. Whisk to combine then slowly drizzle in the oil, whisking constantly until fully emulsified. Set aside.

3. To prepare the salad, place the arugula (or spinach) in a large salad bowl. Toss with about half the dressing. Divide the greens among 4 salad plates; top with grapefruit segments and sliced avocado. Drizzle with the remaining dressing.

Recipe Type	Calories	Total Fat (grams)	Carbs (grams)	Protein (grams)
Mixed	267	21	19	3
Carb	263	21	19	3
Protein	254	22	16	4

Mixed Spring Greens with Champagne-Citrus Vinaigrette

4 servings

Salad:

- ½ pound mixed spring greens (CT), or spinach (PT)
  Sea salt and freshly ground black pepper, to taste
- 2 small oranges, peeled and segmented
- ¼ cup chopped almonds, toasted

Champagne-Citrus Vinaigrette:

- 1 tablespoon champagne vinegar
- 1 tablespoon freshly squeezed orange juice (use the juice from the segmented oranges above)
- ½ teaspoon Dijon mustard
- 1½ teaspoons freshly grated orange peel
- ½ teaspoon sea salt, or to taste
- ½ teaspoon freshly ground black pepper, or to taste
- ½ teaspoon honey
- ⅓ cup extra-virgin olive oil

1. Preheat the oven to 350°F. Spread the chopped almonds in a single layer on an oven safe tray and toast until lightly browned, about 5 minutes. Set aside and allow to cool.

2. Grate 2 teaspoons of peel from the oranges, reserving for the salad dressing. Peel the oranges. Hold the peeled orange in one hand over a bowl. Use a paring knife and in a sawing motion cut each segment from the membrane on both sides. Let the juice drip into the bowl and place segments in another bowl. When all segments have been removed from both oranges squeeze the remaining juice from the membranes and reserve 1 tablespoon of the juice for the dressing.

Continued on page 67

3. Whisk the vinegar, orange juice, mustard, orange peel, salt, pepper, and honey together in a small bowl. Slowly drizzle in the oil, whisking constantly, until the mixture is completely emulsified. Taste, and adjust seasonings if necessary.

4. Place the spring greens in a large salad bowl, and toss with the vinaigrette. Season to taste with salt and pepper.

5. Divide the greens onto 4 salad plates. Toss the oranges in the salad bowl in the remaining dressing, and then add them to the salads. Sprinkle with chopped almonds and serve.

Recipe Type	Calories	Total Fat (grams)	Carbs (grams)	Protein (grams)
Mixed	333	28	17	8
Carb	331	28	18	7
Protein	335	28	18	8

Rainbow Root Vegetable Salad (CT)

5 servings

    5 whole beets (about 2 inches in diameter)
   ¼ cup fresh chives, minced
    3 cups celery root, peeled and grated
    2 tablespoons fresh lemon juice
    2 tablespoons fresh Italian parsley, minced
   ½ teaspoon celery salt
  3½ cups grated carrots
    2 tablespoons fresh tarragon, minced

Shallot-Mustard Vinaigrette:

   ¼ cup minced shallots
   ¼ cup red wine vinegar
    1 tablespoon Dijon mustard
    1 small clove garlic, pressed
   ¼ cup olive oil

1. Whisk shallots, vinegar, mustard, and garlic in a small bowl to blend. Gradually whisk in olive oil. Set aside.

2. Cook beets in a pot of boiling salted water until tender when pierced with a small sharp knife, about 30 minutes. Drain and let cool. Peel and grate beets.

3. Mix beets, chives and 1/3 cup of the Shallot-Mustard Vinaigrette in a medium bowl.

4. Combine celery root, lemon juice parsley, and celery salt in a second medium bowl. Mix with 1/3 cup Shallot-Mustard Vinaigrette.

Continued on page 69

5. Mix carrots, tarragon, and 1/3 cup Shallot-Mustard Vinaigrette in a third medium bowl. Season each salad with salt and pepper.

6. Cover and chill salads for at least 1 hour. (Salads can be prepared 1 day ahead. Keep them separate from each other until ready to serve so that colors stay clean. Keep chilled.)

7. Arrange salads on a platter, placing the beet mix on the bottom, then layer the celery root mix on top of the beets, finishing with the carrot mix on top. Serve immediately.

Recipe Type	Calories	Total Fat (grams)	Carbs (grams)	Protein (grams)
Carb	185	11	21	3

Indian Cabbage Salad

4 servings

- 2 tablespoons coconut oil
- 1 teaspoon black mustard seeds
- 1 teaspoon turmeric
- 4 cups white or red cabbage, shredded
- 1 teaspoon salt

1. In a heavy skillet over medium heat, heat coconut oil.

2. Add mustard seeds and turmeric, sauté for 1 minute.

3. Stir in cabbage; add salt, stir-fry for a couple more minutes.

4. Add a few tablespoons of water, cover, and let cabbage steam for a couplemore minutes.

5. Remove from heat and serve.

Recipe Type	Calories	Total Fat (grams)	Carbs (grams)	Protein (grams)
Mixed	86	7	6	1

Ravishing Red Salad (CT)

4 servings

- 4 medium red beets, shredded or grated
- 1 medium red onion, chopped finely
- 1 medium red pepper, chopped coarsely
- 1 carton sunflower sprouts
- 4 ounces goat or sheep feta cheese, crumbled
- 1 lemon, juiced
- 3 tablespoons flax seed oil

1. Peel the beets, then grate or shred them in a food processor. Place in large bowl. Add the onion, red pepper, sunflower sprouts, and feta cheese.

2. In a separate bowl, mix the lemon juice and flax seed oil. Pour over beet mixture and serve.

Recipe Type	Calories	Total Fat (grams)	Carbs (grams)	Protein (grams)
Carb	380	27	24	16

Sunflower Power Salad

4 servings

1 large head red cabbage, shredded

1 pound spinach

2 cups packed sunflower sprouts

1 bunch fresh cilantro, chopped

1 cup toasted sunflower seeds

Basil-Cider Vinaigrette:

¼ cup apple cider vinegar

¼ cup olive oil

2 tablespoons water

1 tablespoon Dijon mustard

1 garlic clove, pressed

2 tablespoons fresh basil, chopped

Salt and pepper to taste

1. Preheat oven to 350°F.

2. Place sunflower seeds in a rectangular glass dish and place in oven to brown. About 10 minutes.

3. Meanwhile, combine and mix all of the dressing ingredients in a separate bowl.

4. Place the cabbage, spinach, sunflower sprouts, and cilantro in a large bowl. Mix with dressing and toasted sunflower seeds. Serve immediately.

Recipe Type	Calories	Total Fat (grams)	Carbs (grams)	Protein (grams)
Mixed	558	43	38	17

Watercress, Spinach, and Pear Salad

4 servings

Salad:

  2 cups watercress, trimmed, use sprigs

  2 cups spinach, rough chopped

1½ pounds pears, (1 large or 2 medium)

    Salt and pepper, to taste

  1 carrot, shredded

  1 tablespoon sesame seeds, toasted

Dressing:

  1 tablespoon fresh ginger, roughly chopped

 ¼ cup seasoned rice vinegar

 ¼ cup smooth almond butter

1½ tablespoons sugar (or raw honey)

  2 tablespoons water, or more if needed

 ½ teaspoon chili paste, or to taste

 ½ teaspoon salt

  3 tablespoons toasted sesame oil

1. Place watercress and spinach in a large bowl.

2. Cut pears into thick matchstick like slices. Toss gently with the watercress and spinach. Season with salt and pepper to taste.

3. Place all dressing ingredients in a blender and blend until smooth.

4. Drizzle dressing over salad and garnish with grated carrot and toasted sesame seeds.

Recipe Type	Calories	Total Fat (grams)	Carbs (grams)	Protein (grams)
Mixed	259	20	20	4

Soups

Asian Chicken and Chili Soup

4 servings

- 6 cups chicken broth
- 2 red bell peppers, thinly sliced
- 2 tablespoons tamari soy sauce
- 1-3 teaspoons Asian hot chili sauce
- 3 cups poached chicken breast, diced (CT), or chicken thighs/legs (PT)
- 1 bunch watercress, large stems trimmed (CT), or spinach (PT)
- 2 scallions, thinly sliced

1. In a 3-quart saucepan, bring broth, bell peppers, tamari, and chili sauce to a simmer; cook until peppers are crisp-tender, about 6 minutes.

2. Add chicken and watercress (or spinach); cook 1 minute. Ladle into bowls, and top with scallions.

Recipe Type	Calories	Total Fat (grams)	Carbs (grams)	Protein (grams)
Mixed	255	10	11	38
Carb	246	6	10	40
Protein	295	13	11	36

Asparagus and Cauliflower Soup (PT only)

4 servings

- 1 tablespoon olive oil
- 1 tablespoon coconut oil
- 2 small onions, thinly sliced
- 1 garlic clove, pressed
- 4 cups asparagus, cut into 1" pieces
- 4 cups chicken stock
- ¼ cup organic unsweetened coconut milk
- 2 tablespoons butter
- 1 head cauliflower, steamed
- Salt and pepper to taste

1. In a medium saucepan, over medium heat, heat olive and coconut oil.
2. Add onion, garlic, and asparagus until soft.
3. Add chicken stock and bring to a boil. Lower heat and simmer for additional 15–20 minutes.
4. Add coconut milk and butter. Boil for 2 minutes and remove from heat.
5. In a food processor, puree the entire mix. Add half of the steamed cauliflower and puree again.
6. Return to pot, warming and stirring the mix. Return to processor again, adding a ¼ of the remaining steamed cauliflower and puree.
7. Return the puree to the pot, adding the remaining ¼ of the cauliflower as is. Over low heat, stir the soup until warm and serve.

Recipe Type	Calories	Total Fat (grams)	Carbs (grams)	Protein (grams)
Protein	290	20	22	11

Broccoli Soup

6 servings

1½ pounds broccoli (CT), or cauliflower (PT), cut into small florets

1 large yellow onion, coarsely chopped

2 medium potatoes, cut into 2-inch pieces

3 cups vegetable or chicken stock

½ cup white wine

¼ teaspoon freshly squeezed lemon juice

¼ cup basil, chopped

Salt and pepper to taste

1 cup raw cream

1 fresh lemon for garnish

1. In a large pot combine the broccoli or cauliflower, onion, potatoes, vegetable stock, wine, lemon juice, salt, and pepper. Bring to a boil. Decrease the heat to low, and simmer covered until the vegetables are tender, about 25 minutes.

2. Remove the soup from the heat and add the cream. Using a high speed blender, blend the ingredients, wrapping a towel around the top of the blender to prevent spillage. You will probably have to do it in 2 or 3 rounds as you do not want to fill the blender to the top. Add half the basil and blend until smooth.

3. Serve in bowls garnished with lemon slices and basil leaves.

Recipe Type	Calories	Total Fat (grams)	Carbs (grams)	Protein (grams)
Mixed	263	6	27	8
Carb	266	6	27	8
Protein	262	6	27	8

Chicken Soup with Yellow Lentils

4 servings

1 whole chicken, cut up (marinate overnight in lemon juice if you have time)

2 tablespoons olive oil

1 medium onion, chopped

1 can crushed tomatoes

3 tablespoons apple cider vinegar

1 tablespoon balsamic vinegar

½ cup yellow lentils, soaked overnight

4 cups chicken stock

½ head medium cabbage, chopped (CT), or ½ lb spinach (PT)

4 cloves garlic, minced

1. Heat a large pot over medium heat and add olive oil. Place chicken in pot and brown each side for 5 minutes. Remove and set aside.

2. Place onions in the pot and sauté for 4–5 minutes. Add the tomatoes and sauté for another 5–10 minutes. Add both vinegars, lentils, stock, and chicken. Simmer for 1 hour on low heat.

3. Remove chicken and take off skin and bones. Then return the chicken to the pot.

4. Add the cabbage and cook for 15 minutes. Add the garlic and spinach (if using). Cook for another 10 minutes.

5. Serve over brown rice or alone with some parmesan cheese sprinkled on top.

Recipe Type	Calories	Total Fat (grams)	Carbs (grams)	Protein (grams)
Mixed	550	15	25	36
Carb	500	15	34	36
Protein	400	15	29	36

Healthy Recipes for Your Nutritional Type

Creamy Zucchini-Cashew Soup

6 servings

- 3 tablespoons coconut oil or raw butter
- 6 cups sliced zucchini
- 1 cup celery, thinly sliced
- 1 teaspoon celery seeds, ground (optional)
- ½ green bell pepper, sliced
- 4 cups vegetable stock
- 1½ cups cashews, toasted (optional)
- ½ teaspoon salt

1. Melt the coconut oil or butter in a large soup pot. Add the celery seeds, zucchini, celery, bell pepper, and salt. Stir, cover and cook over low heat until the vegetables are tender, about 30 minutes.

2. Puree the cashews in the vegetable stock in a blender or food processor.

3. Combine the vegetables and the cashew-stock mixture in a blender. Puree thoroughly.

4. *Place a large sieve (wire mesh strainer) over the soup pot. Strain the vegetable-cashew mixture through it, stirring, and pressing the mixture down with the back of a spoon. Scrape bottom of sieve frequently. This step allows the soup to become creamy.

5. Discard the remaining "material" that pulls from the sieve.

6. Reheat the soup to serving temperature.

*If using cashew butter, mix in the cashew butter after step 3 and reheat in soup pot.

Recipe Type	Calories	Total Fat (grams)	Carbs (grams)	Protein (grams)
Mixed	424	33	22	15

Chilled Sun Gold Tomato Soup with Avocado-Chili Salsa

4–6 servings

   4 pints Sun Gold tomatoes
   4 medium shallots, minced
   1 teaspoon sea salt
   1 cup water
   6 tablespoons white wine vinegar
   4 teaspoons Serrano pepper, seeds removed and minced
   ¼ cup extra virgin olive oil
   2 avocados, ripe
   2 tablespoons cilantro, finely chopped
      Sea salt and freshly ground pepper

1. Remove the stems from the tomatoes and rinse. Add them to a heavy saucepan with a tight-fitting lid. Also add half of the shallots, ½ teaspoon of salt and 1 cup of water. Cook over medium high heat. Soon you will hear the tomatoes popping. After a couple of minutes take a look to make sure there is enough moisture, if not add a little more water. After the skins have popped and the tomatoes have released their juices, lower the heat and cook for about 20 minutes keeping the lid on the pot.

2. Run the tomatoes through a food mill or mesh sieve. Push juices through thoroughly by pressing the tomatoes against the mesh with a spoon. You will have about 2 cups of puree. Chill well.

Continued on page 83

3. Just before serving, combine the remaining shallots in a bowl with the vinegar, the Serrano pepper, oil, avocado and cilantro. Season with a pinch or two of salt and some pepper. Spoon the soup into chilled cups; add a dollop of the avocado mixture and serve.

PT: After chilling soup and before adding the avocado mixture, whisk 1 cup of raw milk plain yogurt into the puree.

Recipe Type	Calories	Total Fat (grams)	Carbs (grams)	Protein (grams)
Mixed	226	19	14	3
Protein	251	21	16	5

Cioppino

6 servings

 5 large cloves garlic, minced
 2 medium onions, chopped
 1 bay leaf
 1 teaspoon dried oregano
 1 teaspoon red pepper flakes
1½ teaspoons salt
 ½ teaspoon black pepper
 4 tablespoons coconut oil
 2 green bell pepper, deseeded and chopped
 2 tablespoons tomato paste
1½ cups dry red wine
 1 28-oz can fire roasted tomatoes, crushed
 1 cup clam juice* (optional)
 1 cup chicken broth
 ½ pound crab meat
 1 pound red snapper, cut into 1" pieces
30 shrimp, shelled and de-veined
 1 pound sea scallop
 3 tablespoons chopped parsley
 3 tablespoons chopped basil

1. In a large pan over medium heat, sauté the onions, garlic, red pepper flakes, oregano, bay leaf, salt, and pepper in coconut oil, stirring often, until onions are transparent, about 6–7 minutes.

Continued on page 85

2. Add the bell peppers and tomato paste, stir for 1 minute. Add wine and boil until it reduces to about half, about 5–6 minutes. Add tomatoes, clam juice, chicken broth, and simmer covered for 30 minutes. Season with salt and pepper.

3. Add crab, snapper, shrimp, scallop, salt, and pepper. Cover and simmer until cooked through, about 5–7 minutes. Discard bay leaf, then stir in parsley and basil. Serve immediately.

Recipe Type	Calories	Total Fat (grams)	Carbs (grams)	Protein (grams)
Mixed	424	12	22	45

Fresh and Chunky Gazpacho (CT)

4 servings

- 3 cups chopped tomatoes
- 1 cup chopped cucumber, peeled and seeded
- ⅔ cup finely chopped yellow onion
- ½ cup chopped red bell pepper
- ½ cup chopped yellow bell pepper
- ½ cup chopped celery
- 2 teaspoons olive oil
- 2 teaspoons horseradish
- 2 teaspoons balsamic vinegar
- 2 teaspoons brown rice vinegar
- ¼ teaspoon sea salt
- ¼ teaspoon freshly ground pepper
- 2 cups tomato juice
- 1 clove garlic, minced

Garnish:

- ¼ cup plain yogurt (PT), or plain non-fat yogurt (CT)
- ¼ cup chopped fresh cilantro
- ½ avocado, chopped

1. In a large bowl, combine all ingredients, except garnish items. Cover and chill at least 2 hours, or overnight.

2. Serve in chilled bowls and top each serving with a dollop of yogurt, 1 tablespoon cilantro, and a few avocado pieces.

Recipe Type	Calories	Total Fat (grams)	Carbs (grams)	Protein (grams)
Mixed	95	3	17	3

Hazelnut Squash Soup

4 servings

1½ cups mashed cooked acorn squash
1 cup finely chopped hazelnuts
½ cup finely chopped onion
1 quart chicken stock
Salt, to taste
¼ teaspoon pepper
2 tablespoons sherry
1 teaspoon white miso

1. Combine squash, hazelnuts, onion and stock in saucepan. Bring to a boil; cover and simmer 30 minutes, stirring occasionally.

2. Stir in salt to taste, pepper, sherry, and miso. Puree mixture in food processor.

Note: Hazelnuts are also known as filberts. If they are hard to find, cashews would be an acceptable substitution.

Recipe Type	Calories	Total Fat (grams)	Carbs (grams)	Protein (grams)
Mixed	324	21	26	12

Hot and Sour Soup

6 servings

- ½ pound small shrimp, shelled and de-veined
- 2 quarts chicken or vegetable stock
- 2 jalapeno peppers, deseeded and chopped
- ½ teaspoon salt
- 1 lime, zested
- 4 kaffir lime leaves* (optional)
- 3 lemongrass stalks*, bruised and chopped in 2" pieces
- ½ pound scallops
- 2 tablespoons fish sauce* (optional)
- 1 tablespoon tamari
- 1 lime, juiced
- 3 teaspoons cilantro, chopped
- 1 red chili, seeded and slivered
- 6 shiitake mushrooms, sliced
- 2 green onions, sliced

1. Combine stock, jalapeños, salt, lime zest, lime leaves and lemongrass in a heavy pot. Bring to a boil, reduce heat, cover and simmer for 20–30 minutes.

2. Strain. Return liquid to pot over medium heat and bring to a boil. Add shrimp and scallops and cook 1 minute. Stir in fish sauce, tamari, and lime juice.

3. Add cilantro, chili, shiitakes, and green onions.

4. Stir and pour into a tureen or ladle into individual dishes.

Can be found at Asian markets.

Note: Can be served as is or over wild rice or brown rice.

Recipe Type	Calories	Total Fat (grams)	Carbs (grams)	Protein (grams)
Mixed	480	18	45	34

Tuscan Bean and Kale Soup

6 servings

 1 pound dried cannellini beans
 2 tablespoons extra virgin olive oil
 1 large onion, minced
 2 large garlic cloves, minced
 1 tablespoon minced fresh sage
 2 teaspoons minced fresh rosemary
 7 cups chicken stock
 ⅓ pound kale, ribs removed, coarsely chopped
    Salt and freshly ground black pepper

1. Soak beans overnight in water to cover generously; drain.

2. Heat 2 tablespoons oil in a large pot over moderate heat. Add onion and sauté until soft, about 5 minutes. Add garlic, sage and rosemary and sauté 1 minute. Add beans and stock. Bring to a simmer, cover and adjust heat to maintain a gentle simmer. Cook until beans are almost tender, about 1 hour, then add kale. Cover and continue cooking at a gentle simmer until beans and vegetables are tender, about 20 minutes more. Add a little water if soup gets too thick.

3. Remove pot from heat. With a wooded spoon, mash some of the beans against the side of the pot until soup is as thick as you like. Season to taste with salt and pepper.

CT: Reduce beans to 8 ounces and add 1 cup wild rice.

PT: Substitute kale with spinach.

Recipe Type	Calories	Total Fat (grams)	Carbs (grams)	Protein (grams)
Mixed	365	9	52	20
Carb	358	9	53	18
Protein	360	9	53	20

Spicy Miso Kale Soup

6 servings

- 1 medium onion, chopped
- 3 cloves garlic, minced
- 1 tablespoon coconut oil
- 1 teaspoon garam masala *
- 1 teaspoon turmeric*
- ½ teaspoon cayenne pepper
- 2 quarts chicken or vegetable stock, heated in large pan
- 1 bunch kale (CT), or 1 pound spinach, chopped (PT)
- 2 cans garbanzo beans
- 1 can coconut milk
- 2 tablespoons white miso paste
- ¼ cup chopped cilantro

1. Sauté onions and garlic in coconut oil until well cooked over medium heat. Add spices and cook for 2 more minutes.

2. Add the stock and simmer for 5 minutes.

3. Add the kale or spinach and simmer for 5 minutes.

4. With a slotted spoon remove most of the kale or spinach and place in a high speed blender with ¾ of the garbanzo beans and 1 cup of water. Then return to the pan.

5. Add pureed beans, whole beans, and coconut milk; simmer.

6. Remove a small amount of soup and place in a small bowl. Dissolve the miso in that liquid, then add directly into the soup.

Continued on page 91

7. DO NOT BOIL the miso—this will kill the healthy bacteria.

8. Garnish with chopped cilantro and serve.

Can be found in the spice aisle at the grocery store, in an Indian market, or health food store.

Recipe Type	Calories	Total Fat (grams)	Carbs (grams)	Protein (grams)
Mixed	393	17	43	20
Carb	385	17	42	19
Protein	387	17	42	20

Spinach-Basil Green Minestrone Soup

4 servings

2 tablespoons extra virgin olive oil

4 ounces thick cut nitrate/nitrate-free prosciutto, chopped into 1 inch pieces

1 medium yellow onion, chopped

2 stalks of celery with leaves, chopped

2 cloves of garlic, finely minced

1 medium zucchini, diced

1 bay leaf

1 can cannellini beans (or other white bean)

1 can garbanzo beans (chickpeas)

Sea salt and freshly ground pepper

8 cups chicken broth

1 cup mini penne pasta (or wheat-free pasta of your choice)

½ pound green beans, trimmed and cut into 1-inch pieces

10 ounces spinach, stems removed and coarsely chopped (PT), or chard (CT)

½ cup grated Parmesan or Romano cheese (optional)

¼ cup chopped fresh basil (or parsley)

1. Heat a large pot over medium high heat. Add the oil and prosciutto. Sauté for 2 minutes, then add onions, celery, garlic, zucchini and the bay leaf into the pot. Season with salt and pepper, to taste. Sauté for 5 minutes, stirring frequently.

2. Next add the white beans, garbanzo beans and chicken broth to the pot. Cover and bring to a boil.

Continued on page 93

3. Add pasta and green beans and cook for 8 minutes, or until pasta is al dente (just tender). Stir in spinach to wilt, about 1 minute. Stir in cheese and serve in soup bowls. Top each serving with basil or parsley.

CT: Substitute chard for spinach.

PT: Add cooked and shredded turkey dark meat.

Recipe Type	Calories	Total Fat (grams)	Carbs (grams)	Protein (grams)
Mixed	443	17	48	31
Carb	443	17	48	31
Protein	443	17	47	31

Yellow Pepper Soup
with Cucumbers and Yogurt (CT)

4 servings

- 1   teaspoon fennel seeds, crushed
- 4-7   medium yellow sweet peppers, seeded and chopped
- ¼   cup shallots
- ¾   teaspoon ground cardamom
- 2   tablespoons olive oil
- 2   cups chicken broth
- 1   cup water
- 2   tablespoons apple cider vinegar
- ¼   cup cucumber, chopped (CT only)
- 1   8-ounce carton of plain yogurt (PT), or low-fat   (CT)
  Fennel seeds

1. In a bowl, stir together the yogurt and the 1 teaspoon of fennel seeds. Cover and let stand for 30 minutes.

2. Meanwhile, in a large saucepan cook the yellow peppers, shallots, and cardamom in the olive oil for about 15 minutes or until peppers begin to soften, stirring occasionally. Add the broth, water, and vinegar. Bring to a boil; reduce heat and simmer for 5 minutes, covered. Remove from heat and allow to cool slightly.

3. Put half of the pepper mixture into a blender or food processor. Blend until smooth. Repeat by adding the remaining pepper mixture. Return all to saucepan.

Continued on page 95

4. Cook and stir over medium heat until heated thoroughly.

5. Ladle soup into bowls and top with yogurt mixture, the chopped cucumber, and remaining fennel seeds.

PT: This is not an ideal recipe for you. Eat only occasionally.

Recipe Type	Calories	Total Fat (grams)	Carbs (grams)	Protein (grams)
Carb	190	10	23	8
Protein	189	11	22	7

Under the Sea Miso Soup

4 servings

- 6 cups mushroom stock (or vegetable stock)
- 2 3-inch pieces kombu, snipped into pieces*
- ¼ cup snipped wakame*
- 1 inch piece of ginger, minced
- ½ cup grated carrot
- ½ cup diced onion
- ¼ cup dulse*
- 3 tablespoons miso, or to taste
  Toasted sesame oil, to drizzle
- ¼ cup scallions, chopped
- 4 ounces shrimp, peeled and deveined (PT), or 4 ounces cooked cubed cod (CT)

1. Bring stock to a brief boil. Add Kombu, wakame, and ginger. Reduce heat and simmer about 20 minutes.

2. Meanwhile, prepare the remaining vegetables. When the seaweeds are tender add the carrot, onion, and dulse and simmer another 10 minutes.

3. Add the shrimp and cook just until pink, another 2–4 minutes.

4. Remove from heat and dissolve the miso into the soup by stirring it through a strainer. Add the scallions and sesame oil to taste.

Kombu, wakame and dulse are different types of seaweed. They can be found in most grocery stores in the Asian-food aisle.

Recipe Type	Calories	Total Fat (grams)	Carbs (grams)	Protein (grams)
Mixed	228	9	24	14
Carb	219	8	24	13
Protein	226	9	24	13

Healthy Recipes for Your Nutritional Type

Vegetables

Asian-Style Green Bean Sauté

6 servings

1 pound green beans trimmed and cut into 2-inch pieces (PT), or yellow squash, julienned (CT)

1 tablespoon unrefined extra virgin coconut oil

2 cloves garlic, minced

2-inch piece of ginger, minced

3 tablespoons tamari soy sauce

¼ cup fresh lemon juice

Sesame seeds

Sea salt and freshly ground pepper

1. Heat a medium heavy bottom sauté pan over medium high heat. Add oil and heat until glistening. Add green beans and cook for 2 minutes.

2. Add the garlic, ginger and tamari and continue to cook until beans are tender-crisp, about 4 minutes. Remove from heat and add lemon juice. Add salt and pepper to taste.

3. Put in a serving bowl and sprinkle with sesame seeds.

Recipe Type	Calories	Total Fat (grams)	Carbs (grams)	Protein (grams)
Mixed	345	20	38	15
Carb	325	19	38	13
Protein	361	20	41	17

Creamed Spinach

4 servings

¾   cup raw whole milk (PT), or low-fat milk (CT)

¼   cup water

   2 medium garlic cloves, minced

   1 tablespoon butter

1½ tablespoons arrowroot

   2 pounds spinach, steamed (PT), or 2 pounds chard, steamed (CT), drained

¼   cup grated Parmesan cheese

¼   teaspoon ground nutmeg

   Sea salt and freshly ground pepper

1. In a medium saucepan, combine milk, water and garlic. Heat slowly until very hot and steamy. Let stand, covered, for 5 to 10 minutes. This allows the garlic to soften.

2. Melt butter in another medium saucepan over medium high heat. Whisk in flour, then add hot milk mixture, whisking until smooth. Stir in spinach or chard, and cook until sauce is thick and bubbly and the spinach is tender but still green, about 6 minutes.

3. Stir in cheese and season with nutmeg, salt and pepper. Serve immediately.

Recipe Type	Calories	Total Fat (grams)	Carbs (grams)	Protein (grams)
Carb	130	6	14	9
Protein	140	7	13	11

Eggplant and White Bean Stew

4 servings

- 2 cloves garlic, minced
- 1 tablespoon olive oil
- 1 medium onion, cut into thin wedges
- 1 pound of eggplant, peeled and cut into 3/4-inch cubes* (CT), or portabella mushrooms (PT)
- 2 14½-ounce cans of vegetable broth (no MSG)
- 1 15-ounce can navy, cannellini, or Great Northern beans, rinsed and drained
- 3 tablespoons tomato paste
- 2 teaspoons fresh marjoram
- ½ teaspoon ground black pepper

  Parsley sprigs for garnish

1. In a large saucepan cook and stir garlic in hot olive oil over medium heat for 30 seconds. Add onion. Cook for another 2 minutes. Stir in eggplant. Cook for another 3 minutes.

2. Stir in vegetable broth, beans, tomato paste, marjoram, and pepper. Bring to boil; reduce heat. Simmer, covered, until eggplant is tender, about 5 minutes.

3. Serve with fresh parsley sprigs.

Recipe Type	Calories	Total Fat (grams)	Carbs (grams)	Protein (grams)
Mixed	340	7	55	16
Carb	345	7	57	16
Protein	335	7	54	16

Fennel-Dill Artichokes (PT)

4 servings

- 4   artichokes
- 1   cup carrots, quartered lengthwise
- 1   cup fennel or celery, thinly sliced
- ¼   cup olive oil
- ¼   cup melted coconut oil
- ¼   cup fresh lemon juice
- 1   teaspoon fennel seeds
- 2   tablespoons or more fresh dill, chopped
- ½   teaspoon salt
-    Black pepper

1. Trim the tips of the leaves and cut off the stems of the artichokes, so they sit upright.

2. Place in a large pot, add water to cover, and bring to a boil. Cover, reduce heat, and simmer until just barely tender, about 15 minutes. Drain.

3. Preheat the oven to 350°F.

4. Mix the carrots, fennel, and celery. Spread evenly in a baking dish with a lid. Place the artichokes upright on top of the vegetables.

5. Mix the olive oil, coconut oil, lemon juice, fennel seeds, dill, salt, and a few sprinkles of black pepper. Pour over artichoke mixture.

6. Cover the baking dish and bake until all the vegetables are tender, about 45 minutes.

PT: This is a high starch dish, so eat in small amounts and combine with a protein and fat meal.

Recipe Type	· Calories	Total Fat (grams)	Carbs (grams)	Protein (grams)
Protein	342	28	24	6

Garlic Green Beans with Parsley (PT)

4 servings

- 1 pound green beans, stem ends removed
- 2 tablespoons olive oil
- 2 medium cloves of garlic, minced
- 2 teaspoons lemon zest
  Sea salt and freshly ground pepper
- 1 tablespoon lemon juice
- 2 tablespoons chopped Italian parsley

1. Bring a large pot of salted water to boil. Add green beans and cook until tender but still crisp, about 4 minutes. Drain and set aside.

2. In the same pot, heat 1 tablespoon of oil over medium low heat. Add the garlic and cook until it begins to soften, about 2 minutes. Return the beans to the pot. Add the lemon zest, remaining 1 tablespoon oil, and season with salt and pepper. Remove from heat and stir in the lemon juice and parsley. Toss to coat and serve.

PT: Sprinkle with 1/4 cup almonds, toasted and chopped, and sprinkle with raw cheese of choice.

Recipe Type	Calories	Total Fat (grams)	Carbs (grams)	Protein (grams)
Protein	82	7	5	1

Garlic Spice Collard Greens

5 servings

- 1 large bunch collard greens (about 1.5 pounds) (CT), or spinach (PT)
- 2 tablespoons olive oil
- 1 medium clove garlic, chopped
- ½ teaspoon dried chili flakes
- Sea salt and pepper, to taste
- Juice of 1 lemon
- Feta cheese (PT)

1. Wash the greens thoroughly under running water and pat dry. Remove the stems and cut the greens into 1-inch strips.

2. Heat a large sauté pan over medium high heat. Add the oil and heat until shimmering. Add the garlic and cook only until it just begins to brown, about 30 seconds. Add the collard greens and chili flakes and cook only until the greens wilt. Add salt and pepper to taste and remove from heat.

3. Add the lemon juice and transfer to a serving bowl.

PT: Sprinkle raw feta cheese on top.

Recipe Type	Calories	Total Fat (grams)	Carbs (grams)	Protein (grams)
Mixed	70	7	3	2
Carb	62	6	3	1
Protein	78	7	2	2

Hijiki-Shiitake Sauté (MT)

4 servings

- 1 cup hijiki (seaweed found in Asian stores)
- 3 cups water
- 1 medium onion, sliced
- 1 carrot, sliced into matchstick
- 1 tablespoon toasted sesame oil
- 2 shiitake mushrooms, sliced
- 1 cup apple juice
- 2 tablespoons tamari soy sauce
- 1 teaspoon fresh ginger, grated

1. Soak the hijiki for 10 minutes in water. Strain and keep water.

2. Sauté onions and carrots in sesame oil until onions are transparent.

3. Add hijiki, shiitakes, and soaking water plus apple juice to cover mixture.

4. Bring to a boil, cover and simmer gently for 45 minutes.

5. Stir in tamari and juice from ginger. Simmer until most of the liquid is evaporated, about 15 minutes.

6. Serve warm or chilled.

Recipe Type	Calories	Total Fat (grams)	Carbs (grams)	Protein (grams)
Mixed	99	4	14	4

Ginger Baby Bok Choy

4 servings

6	heads baby bok choy
1½	tablespoons seasoned rice vinegar
1½	tablespoons tamari soy sauce
1	tablespoon mirin*
½	teaspoon honey
2	tablespoons toasted sesame oil
1	tablespoon olive oil
1	pinch red pepper flakes
3	cloves garlic
1	tablespoon minced ginger
2	scallions
1	teaspoon lemon juice
1	tablespoon toasted sesame seeds

Note: Have all ingredients ready as the stir frying is rather quick.

1. Cut the bottoms off bok choy heads. Separate the leaves and cut across into small pieces, keeping stems and leaves separate.

2. Mix together the vinegar, tamari, mirin, honey and toasted sesame oil in a bowl and set aside.

3. Over high heat, warm the sauté pan or wok, add the olive oil, making sure it covers the pan. Add the bok choy, red pepper flakes, scallions, garlic and ginger. Stir fry for 30 seconds.

Continued on page 107

4. Add sauce mixture and cook for about 1 minute, until mixture thickens. Add bok choy leaves and for cook another 30 seconds, until the bok choy is wilted.

5. Place the bok choy in a serving bowl, add a squeeze of lemon and sprinkle with sesame seeds. Serve immediately.

Can be found in the Asian food aisle at the grocery store or in an Asian market.

Recipe Type	Calories	Total Fat (grams)	Carbs (grams)	Protein (grams)
Mixed	135	5	13	6

Mint Snap Peas

4 servings

> 1 pound snow or sugar snap peas
> ¼ cup tamari soy sauce
> ¼ cup brown rice vinegar
> 2 teaspoons toasted sesame oil
> 1 teaspoon sugar
> 1 teaspoon rice wine (sake)
> ¼ cup chopped fresh mint
> 2 tablespoons sesame seeds (PT)

1. Snap ends off the peas and remove the strings. Bring a medium pot of salted water to a boil and add peas. Cook for about 2 minutes, or until tender-crisp. Drain in a colander and rinse in cold water to stop the cooking. Lay out on paper towels and blot dry.

2. In a medium bowl, whisk together the tamari, rice vinegar, sesame oil, sugar, and rice wine. Add the peas and mint and toss to coat. Can be served hot, at room temperature, or chilled.

Recipe Type	Calories	Total Fat (grams)	Carbs (grams)	Protein (grams)
Mixed	140	4	12	6
Protein	130	4.5	13	5

Pesto Baked Tomato-Vegetable Casserole (CT)

1 eggplant, sliced into chunks
2 pounds zucchini, sliced into chunks
1 red pepper, sliced into strips
2 medium onions, sliced
4 medium tomatoes, diced
1 cup olive oil
2 garlic cloves
½ cup pesto sauce

Pesto:

2 cups fresh basil (CT), or spinach (PT)
2 garlic cloves, sliced
⅔ cup olive oil
¼ cup pine nuts

1. Blend all ingredients in a blender or food processor.

2. Heat olive oil in a medium saucepan. Add eggplant, zucchini, red pepper, and onions. Sauté over medium heat in small batches, so there is enough olive oil remaining for all the vegetables.

3. Heat the oven to 350°F. Place the sautéed vegetables in a baking dish, leaving the oil used for the vegetables in the saucepan.

4. Add the tomatoes to the oil in the saucepan, press the garlic cloves into the pan, and add salt and pepper to taste.

5. Pour tomato mixture and pesto over the vegetables. Place in the oven and bake for 45 minutes or longer for a more crispy texture.

Recipe Type	Calories	Total Fat (grams)	Carbs (grams)	Protein (grams)
Carb	566	55	20	5

Rainbow Chard with Red Onions

4 servings

- 1 medium red onion, sliced into half moons
- 1 tablespoon olive oil
- 1 bunch chard, chopped finely (CT), or spinach (PT)
- 1 tablespoon tamari soy sauce
- 1 teaspoon lemon juice

1. Place chopped onion into skillet with olive oil. Cook for about 3 minutes.

2. Add the chard, cook for another 2 minutes, then add tamari and lemon juice. Cook for another 2 minutes.

3. Place into a medium-sized bowl and serve.

Recipe Type	Calories	Total Fat (grams)	Carbs (grams)	Protein (grams)
Mixed	75	4	9	3
Carb	80	4	10	3
Protein	66	4	6	3

Red Peppers and Broccoli with Ume Tarragon Dressing

4 servings

Salad:

  2 cups water

  ¼ teaspoon sea salt

  2 cups red pepper, matchstick sliced

  2 cups broccoli, stems and florets (CT), or cauliflower (PT)

Dressing:

  ¼ cup olive oil

  1 teaspoon umeboshi plum*

  ¼ teaspoon ground fresh pepper

  4 sprigs fresh tarragon

1. Bring water to boil and add salt. Quickly blanch the broccoli stems and florets (to blanch, place veggies in the boiling water for about 1–2 minutes, remove and plunge into ice water. Once the broccoli has cooled, remove and drain). The broccoli should be bright and crunchy.

2. Arrange red peppers and broccoli in clear bowl.

3. Mix dressing ingredients and toss with veggies. Let stand for 5–10 minutes so the dressing can marinade the veggies.

4. Garnish with tarragon leaves and serve.

Can be found in the Asian aisle at the grocery store or in an Asian market.

Recipe Type	Calories	Total Fat (grams)	Carbs (grams)	Protein (grams)
Mixed	165	14	11	3
Carb	169	14	11	3
Protein	167	14	11	4

Roasted Asparagus and Fennel (PT)

6 servings

- 1 bunch asparagus, trimmed
- 2 medium oranges, sliced thinly
- 1 medium fennel bulb
- 1 cup orange juice
- ¼ cup olive oil, plus 2 tablespoons
- 2 tablespoons sherry vinegar, or apple cider vinegar
- ¼ teaspoon fennel seeds,* toasted and crushed in mortar and pestle or spice grinder
- ½ teaspoon honey (optional)
- ½ teaspoon sea salt
- ¼ teaspoon black pepper, freshly ground
- 1 tablespoon pistachio nuts, chopped

1. Preheat oven to 450°F.

2. Toss asparagus with the 2 tablespoons of olive oil and a pinch of salt. Line an oven safe dish with parchment paper and spread the asparagus out in a single layer. Roast until tender, about 8–10 minutes.

3. Peel and section oranges over a bowl, to reserve juice.

4. Trim brown ends from the fennel bulb and cut vertically, into very thin slices.

5. To make dressing, bring 1 cup of orange juice to a boil over high heat. Reduce heat to medium low and simmer until juice is reduced by half, about 20 minutes. Transfer to a small bowl and cool. When cool, slowly add olive oil, whisking constantly. When blended, add vinegar, fennel seeds, honey, salt, and pepper. Whisk to blend. *Continued on page 113*

6. Place oranges and fennel in a large bowl and toss with dressing.

7. Serve and garnish with pistachio nuts.

Can be found in the spice aisle of the grocery store, health food store, or Indian market.

Recipe Type	Calories	Total Fat (grams)	Carbs (grams)	Protein (grams)
Protein	217	16	18	4

Roasted Cauliflower with Celeriac and Dulse

4 servings

- 1 large head cauliflower (CT), or broccoli (PT)
- 1 bulb celeriac (celery root)*
- 2 tablespoons olive oil
- 1 clove garlic, pressed
- 2 tablespoons dulse granules
- 1 tablespoon fresh rosemary, chopped
- Salt and pepper to taste

If you can't find celeriac, you can substitute: turnips or celery ribs

1. Heat the oven to 350°F.

2. Wash the cauliflower and cut into florets. Thinly slice the celeriac bulb.

3. Toss the celeriac with the olive oil, garlic and sprinkle with dulse.

4. Place the cauliflower and celeriac in a casserole dish and bake until brown. About 45 minutes.

5. Remove from oven and season with salt and pepper.

Recipe Type	Calories	Total Fat (grams)	Carbs (grams)	Protein (grams)
Mixed	125	5	11	5
Carb	128	7	15	5
Protein	112	2	7	5

Rosemary Brussels Sprouts with Cream

4–6 servings

- 1½ pounds Brussels sprouts (CT), or cauliflower, chopped (PT)
- 2 tablespoons butter
- 1 cup low-fat coconut milk*(CT), or regular coconut milk (PT)
- 1 tablespoon fresh rosemary, chopped
  Salt and pepper to taste

1. Remove the ends and any tough parts from the Brussels sprouts. Slice crosswise and lengthwise to shred.

2. Melt the butter in a large pan. Add the rosemary and the Brussels sprouts. Sauté over medium heat, stirring constantly until tender.

3. Add the coconut milk. Cook over high heat for about 1–2 minutes. Stir constantly until the coconut milk is slightly reduced.

4. Remove from heat and serve immediately.

*Half and half can be used in place of coconut milk.

Recipe Type	Calories	Total Fat (grams)	Carbs (grams)	Protein (grams)
Mixed	140	12	7	4
Carb	146	12	9	4
Protein	133	12	7	3

Slow Roasted Garlic Tomatoes (CT)

6 servings

8 ripe Roma tomatoes

6 cloves of garlic

2 tablespoons olive oil

6 teaspoons thyme

Salt and pepper

1. Heat the oven to 300°F.

2. Core out each tomato and cut a 3/4 inch deep X in the end of each tomato.

3. Sprinkle inside of tomatoes with salt and pepper.

4. Stuff each tomato with 1 clove of garlic and 1 teaspoon of thyme.

5. Coat olive oil in the bottom of a shallow baking dish, place the tomatoes in a row, and bake 1.5 to 2 hours.

Recipe Type	Calories	Total Fat (grams)	Carbs (grams)	Protein (grams)
Carb	66	5	6	1

Spinach with Butter and Garlic

6 servings

> 2 pounds spinach (PT), or Swiss chard/collard/kale (CT), chopped
>
> 2 tablespoons butter
>
> 2 cloves garlic, chopped coarsely

1. Melt butter in large skillet. Add garlic, cook over medium heat for 1–2 minutes.

2. Add spinach and cook for 2 minutes, or until the leaves are wilted.

Recipe Type	Calories	Total Fat (grams)	Carbs (grams)	Protein (grams)
Mixed	40	4	1	1
Carb	40	4	1	1
Protein	40	4	1	1

Sweet and Sour Brussels Sprouts

4 servings

   1 pound Brussels sprouts, ends trimmed
   2 tablespoons balsamic vinegar
   2 tablespoons maple syrup
   1 teaspoon Dijon mustard
   2 tablespoons coconut oil
   ½ cup peanuts
      Sea salt and freshly ground pepper, to taste

1. In a medium saucepan of boiling salted water, cook Brussels sprouts until tender but still slightly crisp, about 7 minutes. Drain and cut into quarters.

2. In a medium bowl, add the vinegar, syrup, and mustard. Whisk to combine then slowly drizzle the coconut oil until fully emulsified. Add the Brussels sprouts, peanuts, salt, and pepper. Toss to coat. Serve immediately.

CT: Reduce oil and nuts by half.

Recipe Type	Calories	Total Fat (grams)	Carbs (grams)	Protein (grams)
Carb	915	66	72	31
Mixed	591	34	66	22

Grains

Apple, Nut, and Grain Salad

4 servings

>   1 cup cooked wild rice
>   1 cup cooked brown rice
>   1 cup cooked barley
>   2 large Granny Smith apples, peeled, cored and diced
>   ½ cup toasted walnuts, coarsely chopped
>   2 ribs celery, thinly sliced
>   1 small carrot, grated
>   ⅓ cup raisins
>   ½ cup chopped fresh dill
>   ½ cup plain yogurt (PT), or low-fat plain yogurt (CT)
>   3 tablespoons lemon juice
>   Sea salt and freshly ground pepper, to taste

1. In a large bowl, combine the grains, apples, nuts, celery, carrot, raisins, and dill.

2. Blend in yogurt, lemon juice, salt, and pepper to taste.

PT: Add cooked, diced dark-meat chicken; remove the 1 cup of brown rice

Recipe Type	Calories	Total Fat (grams)	Carbs (grams)	Protein (grams)
Mixed	341	11	56	8
Carb	341	11	57	9
Protein	353	14	45	16

Brown Rice and Poached Egg Nest with Dulse

4 servings

  1 cup brown rice
2¼ cups water
  4 teaspoons gomasio (sesame seeds mixed with sea salt)
  ¼ cup freshly ground flax seeds
  ¼ cup parsley, minced
  ¼ cup dulse flakes
  4 eggs
     Salt and pepper to taste

1. Combine rice and water in a 3 quart saucepan. Bring to a boil, stir once. Cover with a tight fitting lid; reduce heat and simmer 45 minutes. Remove from heat and let stand covered 5–10 minutes longer.

2. While the rice is resting, add water to a 2-quart saucepan to half-fill the pan. Bring water to a boil, and reduce to simmer. Break 1 egg into a measuring cup. Carefully slide egg into simmering water, holding the lip of the cup as close to the water as possible. Repeat with remaining eggs, allowing each egg an equal amount of space. Simmer eggs, uncovered, for 3 to 5 minutes or to desired doneness. Remove with a slotted spoon. Season to taste with salt and pepper, if desired.

Continued on page 123

3. Divide rice onto 4 plates and sprinkle each with 1 teaspoon of gomasio and 1 tablespoon each of ground flax seeds, parsley and dulse flakes. Using a spoon create a little "nest" in each, and then add 1 egg to each nest.

CT: Serve with steamed kale.

PT: Serve with steamed spinach.

Recipe Type	Calories	Total Fat (grams)	Carbs (grams)	Protein (grams)
Mixed	349	14	43	14
Carb	367	15	47	15
Protein	370	15	46	16

Greek Grain Salad with Garlic-Dill Vinaigrette

4 servings

Salad:

- 1   cup barley
-    Salt
- ½   cup brown rice
- ½   cup wild rice
- ½   cup pitted kalamata olives, sliced
- ½   cup crumbled feta cheese
- ½   cup ¼-inch diced cucumber
- ½   cup ¼-inch diced tomato
- ¼   cup ¼-inch diced red onion
- ¼   cup chopped dill
- ¼   cup chopped parsley

Dressing:

- 2   tablespoons apple cider vinegar
- 2   tablespoons minced dill
- 2   cloves garlic, minced
- 6   tablespoons extra virgin olive oil
-    Salt and pepper

1. Bring a large pot of water to a boil. Add the barley and cook for 15 minutes. Using a sieve, remove barley from the water and transfer to a bowl.

2. Bring the water back to a boil and salt to taste. Add the barley and brown rice and wild rice and cook, stirring occasionally, until tender, about 30 to 40 minutes. Drain, transfer to a bowl, and cool.

Continued on page 125

3. When completely cool, combine with the remaining ingredients.

4. Meanwhile, make the Dressing: Whisk together the vinegar, dill, and garlic. While whisking, slowly drizzle in the olive oil to until smooth. Season with salt and pepper to taste.

5. Toss the salad with the dressing and serve.

PT: Option add cooked diced lamb.

CT: Option add additional tomatoes and cucumbers.

Recipe Type	Calories	Total Fat (grams)	Carbs (grams)	Protein (grams)
Mixed	604	29	79	14
Carb	650	32	81	14
Protein	690	34	80	20

Quinoa Salad with Mixed Veggies

4 servings

Salad:

- 2 cups cooked quinoa
- 3 green onions, chopped finely
- 1 cup napa cabbage (CT), or spinach (PT), chopped finely
- ½ cup mushrooms, sautéed, sliced thinly

Dressing:

- 1 tablespoon apple cider vinegar
- 1 lemon, juiced
- 3 tablespoons olive oil
- 1 teaspoon honey
- 1 clove garlic, minced

1. Place all ingredients for salad in large bowl and mix.

2. In a small bowl mix together ingredients for dressing.

3. Pour dressing over the quinoa and veggies. Serve immediately.

Recipe Type	Calories	Total Fat (grams)	Carbs (grams)	Protein (grams)
Mixed	461	16	72	13
Carb	463	16	75	13
Protein	458	16	71	12

Wild Rice Gourmet Salad (CT)

8 servings

- ¾ cup wild rice
- ¼ cup brown rice
- 1 cup toasted walnuts, chopped
- 2 tablespoons olive oil
- 2 tablespoons balsamic vinegar
- 1 teaspoon Dijon mustard
- 1 clove garlic, minced
- ¾ cup dried cranberries
- ½ cup chopped Italian parsley
- ⅓ cup chopped scallions

1. In a medium-sized saucepan with a tight-fitting lid, bring 2 cups of water to a boil. Stir in the wild rice and the brown rice, reduce the heat to low. Cover the saucepan and cook for 45 minutes, or until all the water is absorbed.

2. Preheat oven to 400°F. Spread the walnuts in a single layer on a baking sheet and toast until lightly browned, about 5 minutes.

3. In a small bowl, stir together the olive oil, vinegar, mustard and garlic.

4. Transfer the cooked rice to a large bowl. Stir in the toasted nuts, cranberries, parsley and scallions. Pour oil mixture on top and stir to combine. Cover and refrigerate until chilled.

Recipe Type	Calories	Total Fat (grams)	Carbs (grams)	Protein (grams)
Carb	209	13	20	5

Red Meat . . .

(Grass-fed Beef, Ostrich, Bison, Lamb)

Baked Lamb Shanks with Mushrooms and Cauliflower

4 servings

- 4 lamb shanks (PT), or ostrich/chicken (CT)
- 1 cup red wine
- 4 tablespoons olive oil
- 3 tablespoons apple cider vinegar
- 2 cups lamb stock
- 2 tablespoons tomato paste
- ½ teaspoon dried oregano
- 3 sprigs thyme, chopped
- ½ teaspoon ground cumin
- ¼ teaspoon cayenne pepper
- 4 cloves garlic
- 8 medium mushrooms, sliced
- 1 head cauliflower, cut into florets (PT), or broccoli (CT)

1. Place lamb shanks in red wine. Marinate overnight or for several hours. Remove lamb and pat dry with paper towels. Reserve marinade. In a heavy casserole, brown the meat in olive oil. Drain oil.

2. Add tomato paste, stock, marinade. Bring to boil and skim. Add all the seasonings except salt and pepper.

3. Bake at 300°F for 3–4 hours or until lamb shanks are falling off the bone. When there is one hour left of cooking time, place the mushrooms and cauliflower florets around the lamb.

4. Remove lamb and vegetables to a serving dish and set aside. Bring sauce to a boil, skimming if needed, until it has reduced by about half and thickened. Pour over the lamb and vegetables. Season to taste.

Recipe Type	Calories	Total Fat (grams)	Carbs (grams)	Protein (grams)
Mixed	713	52	17	37
Carb	338	19	17	19
Protein	558	40	19	28

Beef and Bean Chili

4 servings

2　pounds ground grass-fed beef (PT) 80/20 (17% fat), or ground turkey breast (CT) 8% fat

2　cups chopped onions

2　tablespoons minced garlic cloves

1　medium jalapeno chili, ribs and seeds removed, minced

1½　tablespoons chili powder

2　teaspoons ground cumin

2　15-ounce cans crushed tomatoes

1　15-ounce can tomato sauce

1　can kidney beans, drained and rinsed

¼　cup plain yogurt (PT), or low-fat yogurt (CT)

¼　cup grated grass-fed cheddar cheese (PT), or low-fat grass-fed cheddar cheese(CT)

1. Heat a heavy 5-quart pot. Add the ground beef. Cook, stirring and breaking up meat, until browned. Drain excess fat, leaving a small amount to cook onions in.

2. Add the onions and cook about 5 minutes. Add the garlic and jalapeno; cook until just tender. Stir in the chili powder and cumin. Continue to cook until fragrant, about 1 minute.

3. Stir in the crushed tomatoes and the tomato sauce. Simmer for about 30 minutes.

4. Add the beans and continue cooking, uncovered, until meat and beans are very tender, and chili is thick, about 30 minutes more. Serve in small bowls. Garnish each bowl with 1 tablespoon each yogurt and cheddar cheese.

Recipe Type	Calories	Total Fat (grams)	Carbs (grams)	Protein (grams)
Mixed	531	17	34	60
Carb	550	25	34	49
Protein	520	22	34	49

Lamb Stew

4 servings

2 pounds boneless lamb stew meat (PT), or ostrich meat (CT), marinated overnight in red or white wine

1 cup flour seasoned with salt and pepper

2 tablespoons coconut oil

2 medium onions, chopped

4 cloves garlic, chopped

2 teaspoons Dijon mustard

3 sprigs rosemary, chopped

1 28-oz can crushed tomatoes

4 cups lamb or chicken stock

2 medium green peppers, seeded and chopped (CT), or 1 pound mushrooms, sliced (PT)

¼ cup chopped flat leaf parsley

1. Cut any excess fat from the lamb and coat in flour.

2. Heat a large high-sided skillet and add the coconut oil. Sauté the lamb, brown on all sides, then remove from pan. Set aside.

3. Sauté onions for 5 minutes. Add the mustard, rosemary, garlic, tomatoes, and sauté for another 5 minutes.

4. Add the stock and the lamb. Bring to boil, and simmer for 2–3 hours. Stir occasionally to make sure it doesn't stick to the bottom.

5. Thirty minutes before the lamb is done, add in the green peppers or the mushrooms.

6. Garnish with parsley.

Recipe Type	Calories	Total Fat (grams)	Carbs (grams)	Protein (grams)
Mixed	500	24	42	36
Carb	530	14	49	32
Protein	375	21	50	34

Recipes for Your Nutritional Type

Beef in Red Wine (PT)

8 servings

- 3 pound stewing beef (the tougher, cheaper cuts of meat)
- 2 cups red wine
- 7 tablespoons coconut oil, divided
- ½ cup flour
- 4 cups beef stock
- ½ teaspoon orange zest
- 3 sprigs thyme, tied together
- ½ teaspoon dried black peppercorns, crushed
- 1 pound maitake mushrooms, chopped (use another type mushroom if maitake not available)
- 3 large onions
- Sea salt and pepper

1. Marinate beef in red wine overnight or for a few hours. Remove the beef from the marinade and pat dry (if beef is wet it won't brown).

2. In a dutch oven on the stove top, melt 3 tablespoons of coconut oil. Add meat and brown in small batches and set aside. Pour out cooking fat when done.

3. Add remaining coconut oil, melt, and mix in flour. Cook the flour and oil on a low heat stirring constantly for several minutes. Add the wine from the marinade and stock. Bring to boil, stir and blend well. Return meat and juices to the pot. Add thyme, crushed peppercorns and orange peel.

Continued on page 135

4. Place the dutch oven in a 300°F oven and cook for 3–4 hours or until meat is tender. While it is cooking, sauté the onions in 1 tablespoon of coconut oil for 4–5 minutes and add the maitake mushrooms, sauté for about 10–15 minutes.

5. Remove the meat from the oven when it is tender. Season with salt and pepper to taste. When meat is tender, remove from oven. Remove thyme. Stir in onions and mushrooms and serve.

Recipe Type	Calories	Total Fat (grams)	Carbs (grams)	Protein (grams)
Protein	651	44	24	38

Braised Beef Moroccan Style

6 servings

- 3 tablespoons coconut oil
- 2½ pounds chuck roast (PT), or ostrich/chicken breast (CT), cut into ¾ inch cubes
- 2 cups chopped shallots
- 4 cloves garlic, chopped
- ½ tablespoon ground coriander
- 1 tablespoon paprika
- 1 teaspoon ground cumin
- ½ teaspoon turmeric
- ½ teaspoon cayenne pepper
- 1 cup red wine
- ½ cup sherry
- 2 cups beef broth
- 1 can diced tomatoes in juice
- 1½ cups golden raisins
- Salt and pepper, to taste

1. Heat a large pot, add 2 tablespoons coconut oil. Sprinkle meat with salt and pepper. Add meat to pot, sauté until no longer pink, about 5 minutes. Transfer meat to bowl.

2. Heat 1 tablespoon oil in same pot. Add shallots and sauté till brown, about 8 minutes.

3. Stir in garlic and next 5 ingredients.

4. Add wine and sherry, boil until reduced to glaze, stirring occasionally, 8–10 minutes.

Continued on page 137

5. Add broth, tomatoes with juice, and raisins. Stir to blend. Add beef and juices, heat to simmer.

6. Reduce heat to medium low. Simmer uncovered, stirring occasionally, until sauce is thick and beef tender, about 1 hour and 15 minutes.

7. Season with salt and pepper.

Recipe Type	Calories	Total Fat (grams)	Carbs (grams)	Protein (grams)
Mixed	499	15	42	44
Carb	470	11	46	36
Protein	620	28	46	36

Fresh Herb and Garlic Beef Tenderloin

6 servings

- 2¼ pounds beef tenderloin (PT), or ostrich (CT)
- ½ cup fresh basil leaves, packed
- 1½ tablespoons fresh thyme
- 1 tablespoon fresh oregano
- 3 garlic cloves
- 2 tablespoons Dijon mustard
- ⅛ teaspoon black pepper
- ¼ cup extra virgin olive oil
- ½ teaspoon sea salt

1. To prepare the beef, trim off excess fat using a sharp knife. Fold the thin tip under to approximate the thickness of the rest of the tenderloin. Tie with butcher's twine, then keep tying the roast with twine every 2 inches or so. This helps the roast keep its shape.

2. In the bowl of a food processor, combine the basil, thyme, oregano, garlic, mustard and pepper. While the food processor in running, slowly drizzle in the oil and continue to process until the herbs and garlic are finely chopped.

3. Rub the herb mixture over the beef and refrigerate 4 hours, up to 24 hours.

4. Preheat the oven to 425°F. Place the beef on an oiled baking sheet. Sprinkle with salt. Bake 25 to 30 minutes, or until the internal temperature reaches 135°F (medium rare). Remove from the oven and let rest 10 minutes. Slice and serve.

Recipe Type	Calories	Total Fat (grams)	Carbs (grams)	Protein (grams)
Mixed	426	28	1	40
Carb	351	16	1	48
Protein	510	41	1	33

Healthy Recipes for Your Nutritional Type

Marinated Grilled Ostrich (CT), or Bison (PT)

4 servings

- 4 ostrich steaks, about 6 ounces each (CT), or bison (PT)
- ½ cup red wine vinegar
- 1 tablespoon honey
- 1 tablespoon Dijon mustard
- 1 tablespoon chopped fresh oregano
- 1 tablespoon chopped fresh rosemary
- 1 clove garlic, finely minced
- ¼ cup extra virgin olive oil

1. Place ostrich steaks in a shallow glass dish. In a small bowl combine the vinegar, honey, mustard, oregano, rosemary, and garlic. While whisking, slowly drizzle in the olive oil until fully blended.

2. Pour marinade over the steaks, cover and refrigerate for 2–4 hours. Turn steaks at least once while marinating.

3. Heat grill to high. Grill the steaks about 4 minutes per side, brushing on marinade every 2 minutes. Serve hot.

Recipe Type	Calories	Total Fat (grams)	Carbs (grams)	Protein (grams)
Mixed	480	25	5	50
Carb	360	20	5	38
Protein	440	24	5	48

Moussaka

5 servings

  2 eggplants, sliced

  2 tablespoons butter

  1 pound ground lamb (grass-fed) (PT), or ground chicken (CT)

  1 large onion, chopped

  1 jalapeno pepper, chopped

  1 tablespoon tomato paste

  1 teaspoon cumin

½ teaspoon cinnamon

  2 tablespoons chopped parsley

¼ cup red wine

¼ cup water

  1 egg, beaten

¼ cup Gruyere cheese, grated

¼ cup bread crumbs from spelt or other wheat-free bread

  3 tablespoons butter

  3 tablespoons flour

1½ cups warm milk

  2 egg yolks

1. Slice eggplant into ½ inch slices; salt, cover and set aside. Melt butter and sauté the lamb until browned. Add onion, jalapeno, tomato paste, cumin, cinnamon, parsley, wine, and water.

2. Simmer until liquid is absorbed. Stir in egg, cheese, and half the bread crumbs. Preheat oven to 350°F.

Continued on page 141

3. To prepare sauce, melt 3 tablespoons butter on low heat. Add flour, stir, and remove from heat. Stir in milk—return to heat. Cook sauce till thick, add salt, and pepper. Combine egg yolks with a little of the sauce and then stir into the rest of the sauce mixture. Cook for 2 minutes on low heat.

4. Brown eggplant slices on both sides in hot oil. Grease casserole dish. Sprinkle bottom with remaining bread crumbs, cover with layer of eggplant, then a layer of meat. Keep going until all is used. Finish with eggplant and cover with sauce, sprinkle with grated cheese and bake for 1 hour at 350°F.

Recipe Type	Calories	Total Fat (grams)	Carbs (grams)	Protein (grams)
Mixed	514	26	29	38
Carb	572	28	29	47
Protein	456	24	29	28

Slow Cooked Brisket (PT)

4 servings

- 2 pounds beef brisket
- 2 limes, juiced
- 1 can tomatoes
- 1 medium onion, sliced
- 3 tablespoons tomato paste
- ½ cup beef stock
- 2 cloves garlic

1. Marinate the beef in the lime juice overnight.

2. Place the brisket in ovenproof dish. Mix together the rest of the ingredients and add them to the brisket.

3. Place in the oven on 275°F for 10 hours (can cook overnight).

4. Remove from oven and serve.

Recipe Type	Calories	Total Fat (grams)	Carbs (grams)	Protein (grams)
Protein	325	8	11	50

Poultry

Chicken with Eggplant

4 servings

4 chicken breasts (CT), or 4 whole legs (PT)
2 tablespoons coconut oil
5 cloves garlic
Salt and pepper
½ teaspoon saffron threads
3 medium eggplant, peeled and cubed
½ cup water

1. Sauté garlic cloves with chicken and coconut oil in a pan on medium heat.

2. When the chicken pieces have browned, season them with salt and pepper and saffron, and add eggplant. Add the water and cover the pan, cook gently on low heat for 35–45 minutes or until chicken is done and eggplant is soft and tender.

3. Serve over quinoa or brown rice.

Recipe Type	Calories	Total Fat (grams)	Carbs (grams)	Protein (grams)
Mixed	297	14	24	21
Carb	241	9	24	20
Protein	352	20	24	22

Chicken Stew

8 servings

> 2 whole chickens, cut into pieces
> 2 cups white wine
> 3 tablespoons raw butter
> 3 tablespoons coconut oil
> 2 cups flour
> 2 teaspoons each sea salt and pepper
> 3 tablespoons raw butter
> 4 cups chicken stock
> 4-5 sprigs thyme, chopped
> 1 teaspoon lemon zest
> 1 teaspoon dried black peppercorns, crushed
> 1 medium cauliflower cut into florets (PT), or ½ medium cabbage, sliced (CT)
> 1 pound fresh mushrooms, sliced
> 2 pounds medium boiling onions
> 4 tablespoons raw butter
> 4 tablespoons olive oil
> 2 tablespoons parsley, finely chopped

1. Marinate the chicken pieces in wine for 4–12 hours.

2. Remove chicken from marinade and pat dry with paper towels. Reserve marinade. On a plate, mix flour, salt, and pepper. Melt butter and oil in large casserole dish. Cover chicken in flour mixture and brown on both sides in butter and coconut oil over medium heat, just a few at a time, reserving on a plate. Pour out browning fat and melt 3 tablespoons butter in the casserole.

Continued on page 147

3. Add 3/4 cup of the flour mixture and cook, stirring constantly, for several minutes, until flour becomes slightly browned. Add wine marinade and chicken stock to casserole, stirring often. Bring to a boil and skim.

4. Add thyme, peppercorns, lemon zest and chicken pieces to pot, cover and bake at 325°F for about 2 hours. Add the cauliflower or cabbage to the casserole about 40 minutes before serving.

5. Meanwhile, sauté the sliced mushrooms in 2 tablespoons olive oil and butter. Peel the onions and sauté them gently in butter and olive oil for about 20 minutes. Directly before serving, add mushrooms and onions to the casserole and stir in chopped parsley.

CT: Eat only the white meat (breast).

PT: Eat only the dark meat (legs and thighs).

Recipe Type	Calories	Total Fat (grams)	Carbs (grams)	Protein (grams)
Mixed	661	39	24	38
Carb	658	39	34	37
Protein	664	39	35	38

Chicken with Crimini and Shiitake Mushrooms

4 servings

8　skinless boneless organic chicken thighs (PT), or breast (CT)

Salt and pepper, to taste

6　teaspoons chopped marjoram, divided

2　tablespoons coconut oil, divided

2　tablespoons olive oil, divided

12　ounces crimini and shiitake mushrooms, thickly sliced

1　cup onion, chopped finely

¾　cup chicken broth

½　cup organic raw whipping cream

3　tablespoons dry sherry/marsala (optional)

1. Season chicken with salt and pepper, and add 2 teaspoons marjoram. Melt 1 tablespoon coconut oil with 1 tablespoon olive oil in large pan over moderate to high heat.

2. Add chicken to pan and sauté until just cooked through, about 7 minutes per side. Transfer chicken to plate; cover with lid to keep warm.

3. Melt remaining 1 tablespoon of coconut oil with 1 tablespoon of olive oil in same pan. Add mushrooms, onions and 2 teaspoons marjoram. Sauté until mushrooms are brown and tender, about 6 minutes. Season with salt and pepper. Transfer to bowl.

Continued on page 149

4. Combine broth, cream and sherry (if using) and remaining 2 teaspoons marjoram in same pan, boil until thickened and reduced to ½ cup, about 5 minutes. Season sauce with salt and pepper.

5. Divide mushrooms among four plates. Top mushrooms with chicken. Spoon sauce over and serve.

Recipe Type	Calories	Total Fat (grams)	Carbs (grams)	Protein (grams)
Mixed	381	22	22	27
Carb	410	21	22	35
Protein	352	22	22	20

Coconut-Infused Chicken Lettuce Wraps

6 servings

> 12 leaves of butter lettuce
> 2 tablespoons extra virgin coconut oil
> 1 pound ground chicken breast (CT), or chicken thighs (PT)
> 2 medium green onions, chopped
> ½ cup canned water chestnuts, drained, rinsed and chopped
> ¼ cup chicken broth
> 2 tablespoons tamari soy sauce
> 1 tablespoon arrowroot
> 2 tablespoons filtered water
> ¼ cup gomasio (sesame seeds and sea salt)

1. Wash lettuce leaves gently so as not to damage or tear them. Dry carefully with a towel.

2. Heat the oil in a sauté pan over medium heat. Add the chicken and sauté until browned, breaking up chicken while cooking. Add green onions, water chestnuts, tamari, and chicken broth. Simmer for 5 minutes.

3. Mix the arrowroot with water and add to chicken mixture. Cook over medium high heat until the sauce thickens.

4. Transfer chicken to a serving bowl set on a large platter and sprinkle gomasio on top. Arrange lettuce leaves on platter around the bowl.

5. Each person takes a lettuce leaf and puts a spoonful of the chicken mixture in it like a taco.

Recipe Type	Calories	Total Fat (grams)	Carbs (grams)	Protein (grams)
Mixed	295	14	12	29
Carb	268	11	12	31
Protein	322	18	12	27

Healthy Recipes for Your Nutritional Type

Cornish Game Hens with Rosemary and Shallots

4 servings

- 4 Cornish game hens split lengthwise (CT), or 6 chicken legs or thighs (PT)
- 2 tablespoons olive oil
- 2 tablespoons raw butter, melted
- 1 tablespoon fresh rosemary, chopped
- 2 tablespoons shallots, chopped
- 1 tablespoon raw butter
- 2 tablespoons flour
- 2 cups chicken stock
- ½ cup white wine

1. Place game hen halves, skin side up, in a baking pan. Brush with mixture of butter and oil, season with chopped rosemary, salt, and pepper. Bake at 375°F for about 1 1/2 hours. Remove to a heated platter and keep warm in oven while making sauce.

2. Sauté the shallots in 1 tablespoon butter for 3–5 minutes, turn off the heat, stir in the flour, then pour wine into the pan. Bring to a boil, stirring constantly with a wooden spoon.

3. Add chicken stock, bring to a rapid boil, and let the sauce reduce for about 10 minutes until it thickens (if the sauce needs to be thicker place 1 tablespoon of flour in a cup and add some of the sauce, blend sauce with flour and add to the pan). Transfer game hens to individual plates and pour sauce over.

Recipe Type	Calories	Total Fat (grams)	Carbs (grams)	Protein (grams)
Mixed	415	26	6	36
Carb	350	28	8	15
Protein	390	28	8	38

Recipes for Your Nutritional Type

Mom's Best Chicken

6 servings

- 6 chicken breasts (CT), or thighs (PT)
- 4 eggs
- ½ cup almond meal
- 2 tablespoons fresh parsley, or 1 teaspoon dried
- 1 tablespoon dried garlic
- 2 tablespoons coconut oil

1. Beat eggs in a shallow bowl.

2. Combine almond meal, parsley, and garlic on a large plate. Mix well.

3. To prepare chicken, dip one breast in beaten eggs, remove and dip into almond meal mixture. Coat both sides.

4. Over medium heat in a large frying pan, heat coconut oil, and add chicken. Sauté each side until brown, about 5 minutes.

5. Remove from heat and place on paper towel to cool.

6. Continue with remaining chicken.

Recipe Type	Calories	Total Fat (grams)	Carbs (grams)	Protein (grams)
Mixed	288	18	10	20
Carb	277	16	11	23
Protein	300	22	10	16

Sweet and Spicy Chicken

4 servings

- 2 pounds organic skinless, boneless chicken breasts (CT), or thighs (PT)
- 2 tablespoons olive oil
- 2 tablespoons raw butter
- 1 teaspoon chili powder
- 1 clove garlic, minced
- ⅓ cup orange juice
- 2 tablespoons lime juice
- ¼ cup white wine
- Toasted sesame seeds

1. In a medium saucepan, over medium heat, melt the butter and oil

2. Sprinkle the chicken with chili powder on both sides and add to pan.

3. Cook the chicken for 1 minute on each side.

4. Reduce the heat to medium, add the garlic, and stir for 1 minute.

5. Add the orange juice, lime juice, and wine to chicken.

6. Cook another 2–3 minutes, evenly on each side.

7. Remove from pan and sprinkle with toasted sesame seeds.

Recipe Type	Calories	Total Fat (grams)	Carbs (grams)	Protein (grams)
Mixed	266	22	3	13
Carb	400	19	5	46
Protein	450	33	5	31

Protein is lower in protein type due to more fat with the skin on chicken thighs for the 2 pound quantity. Chicken breasts are all protein, minimal fat for the same 2 pounds.

Tarragon Chicken with Cream

4 servings

4	chicken whole legs (PT), or breasts (CT)
2	tablespoons coconut oil
	Salt and pepper to taste
½	cup onions, chopped
½	cup dry white wine (optional), or water
1¼	cups chicken stock
1	tablespoon Dijon mustard
¼	cup raw, organic cream
3	tablespoons crème fraiche
1	tablespoon fresh tarragon, minced

1. Heat the coconut oil in pan over medium high setting. Season the chicken with salt and pepper. When pan is hot, place chicken in pan. Let the chicken cook for 3 minutes on each side until chicken is brown and crusty. Remove from pan, cover, and set aside.

2. Remove all but 1 teaspoon of fat from pan. Reduce heat to medium low. Add onions and cook for 2 minutes, add the wine or water and reduce until almost dry, about 3 minutes.

3. Add the stock, mustard, cream and half the tarragon and mix well. Add chicken to the sauce, cover and cook until chicken is cooked through, about 15–20 minutes.

4. When done, remove chicken and stir in crème fraiche. Put the chicken on a plate and pour sauce over top. Sprinkle with remaining tarragon.

Recipe Type	Calories	Total Fat (grams)	Carbs (grams)	Protein (grams)
Mixed	327	19	8	26
Carb	210	10	8	19
Protein	444	29	8	33

Seafood

Chili Garlic Ginger Shrimp

4 servings

- ¼ cup extra virgin olive oil
- 2 inch piece of fresh ginger, minced
- 2 cloves of garlic, minced
- 2 fresh red chilies, seeds removed and thinly sliced
- 16 large shrimp (16 ounces), peeled and deveined (PT), or 16 (16 ounces) pieces of cod or other CT fish (CT)
- 1-2 lemons, to taste
- ½ cup Italian parsley, roughly chopped
  Sea salt and freshly ground pepper

1. Heat a large sauté pan over medium high heat. Add olive oil, ginger, garlic, chili and shrimp. Cook for about 3 minutes, stirring often.

2. Turn the heat to low and add the juice of 1 lemon. Stir in parsley. Remove from heat.

3. Taste the sauce and add salt and pepper, and more lemon juice if desired.

CT: *Serve over steamed collard greens.*

PT: *Serve over steamed spinach.*

Recipe Type	Calories	Total Fat (grams)	Carbs (grams)	Protein (grams)
Mixed	261	15	8	25
Carb	230	15	4	5
Protein	170	14	4	19

Clam and Tomato Stew

4 servings

- ¼   cup extra virgin olive oil
- 1   medium red onion, cut into 1/2-inch dice
- 1½   cups tomato sauce (recipe follows)
- ½   cup dry white wine
- 24   littleneck clams, scrubbed and chipped (instructions follow)

Tomato Sauce:

- ¼   cup extra virgin olive oil
- 1   medium onion, cut into 1/4-inch dice
- 4   cloves of garlic, minced
- 3   tablespoons chopped fresh thyme
- 2   28-ounce cans whole tomatoes
-    Salt to taste

Chipping clams:

It is no fun biting into a clam and chewing on sand. Chipping clams gets them to expel sand that is in their shell. Place the live clams in a large bowl and cover with water. Add 2 tablespoons of cornmeal and let stand for 1 hour. Every 15 minutes gently shake the bowl. The clams think they are being fed and end up purging any sand that was in their shell. Carefully lift the clams out of the water so the sand stays at the bottom of the bowl.

1. To prepare the tomato sauce: In a 3-quart saucepan, heat the olive oil over medium heat. Add onion and garlic. Cook until softened and light brown, about 8 minutes.

2. Add thyme and tomatoes with their juice and bring to a boil, stirring often.

Continued on page 159

Healthy Recipes for Your Nutritional Type

3. Lower the heat and simmer until thickened a bit, about 30 minutes. Season with salt, to taste. Keep warm until ready to add the rest of the dish.

4. In a large heavy-bottomed pan, heat the olive oil over medium high heat until it is glistening.

5. Add the onion and cook until softened, about 5 minutes.

6. Add tomato sauce, white wine, clams and cover. Cook until clams are open, about 8 minutes.

7. Divide clams and broth among 4 bowls and serve immediately.

CT: Serve over steamed chard.

PT: Serve over steamed spinach.

Recipe Type	Calories	Total Fat (grams)	Carbs (grams)	Protein (grams)
Mixed	344	28	13	8

Land and Sea Salad

4 servings

- 1 carrot, julienned
- 1 daikon, julienned
- 1 medium red cabbage, shredded
- 1 bunch green onions, chopped
- 1 jalapeno pepper, deseeded, chopped
- ¼ cup chopped cilantro
- ½ pound crabmeat
- ½ pound bay scallops

Dressing:

- 2 tablespoons olive oil
- 2 tablespoons soy sauce
- 1 clove garlic, minced

1. Poach the crabmeat and scallops, separately, for 30 seconds each. Drain and set aside.

2. Combine the remaining ingredients in a large bowl.

3. Add the crab and scallops to the veggies, mix the dressing, pour over salad and serve.

Recipe Type	Calories	Total Fat (grams)	Carbs (grams)	Protein (grams)
Mixed	289	8	29	28

Lemon Scallops with Parsley

4 servings

- 1 tablespoon coconut oil
- 2 pounds sea scallops (PT), or a CT fish suitable for (CT), cut in pieces
- ¾ teaspoon sea salt
- ½ teaspoon freshly ground pepper
- 1 tablespoon butter
- 1 teaspoon minced garlic
- ¼ cup finely minced yellow onion
- ⅓ cup dry white wine
- 2 tablespoons fresh lemon juice
- 1 tablespoon chopped flat-leaf parsley

1. In a large skillet, heat oil over medium high heat. Add scallops and sprinkle with salt and pepper. Sauté 2 minutes per side. Remove from pan and set aside.

2. In the same pan, melt butter. Add the garlic and the shallots and sauté for about 1 minute. Add wine and cook for 2 minutes more. Return the scallops to the pan and toss to coat. Remove from heat and add the lemon juice and parsley.

PT: Serve over steamed spinach.

CT: Serve over steamed chard.

Recipe Type	Calories	Total Fat (grams)	Carbs (grams)	Protein (grams)
Protein	390	20	3	45
Carb	280	8	8	38

Roasted Cauliflower and Crab with Avocado-Yogurt Dressing (PT)

4 servings

- 1 head cauliflower
- 1 red bell pepper
- 1½ tablespoons olive oil
- 1 avocado
- 1 tablespoon fresh lemon juice
- 3 tablespoons plain yogurt
- ¼ teaspoon paprika
- ⅛ teaspoon cayenne pepper
- Sea salt and fleshly ground black pepper, to taste
- ½ pound fresh lump crabmeat, rinsed

1. Preheat oven to 450°F. Cut cauliflower into florets. Cut bell pepper into ¼-inch strips. Lightly oil a baking pan and add the cauliflower and bell pepper. Drizzle with the olive oil, and season lightly with salt and pepper. Cook until cauliflower is lightly browned, about 15–20 minutes.

2. Meanwhile, mash peeled and seeded avocado into a small bowl. Add the lemon juice, yogurt, paprika, and cayenne pepper. Season to taste with sea salt.

3. In a large serving bowl, add the cooked vegetables, crab, and the dressing. Toss and serve in small bowls immediately.

Recipe Type	Calories	Total Fat (grams)	Carbs (grams)	Protein (grams)
Protein	264	14	21	19

Fish

Coconut–Macadamia Nut Crusted Halibut

4 servings

2 pounds wild halibut
2 tablespoons unrefined, extra virgin coconut oil
Juice of 1 lime
½ teaspoon sea salt
½ cup unsweetened flaked coconut
½ cup macadamia nuts, chopped

1. Preheat oven to 400°F.

2. Rinse and pat dry halibut and place in a baking dish. Drizzle coconut oil over the fish and then add the lime juice and salt. Let marinate for about 15 minutes, no longer. It is important to drizzle oil before lime juice because the lime juice will begin to "cook" the fish. The oil first provides some protection against this.

3. Mix coconut and macadamia nuts together onto a plate. Roll the fish in the nut mixture and then using your hands pat additional mixture into fish. Place back in baking dish and pour remaining nut mixture on top. Cover baking dish with foil.

4. Bake for 12 minutes then turn broiler on. Remove foil and allow the broiler to brown the coating. Serve immediately.

CT: Reduce the coconut oil and macadamia nuts by one-half.

Recipe Type	Calories	Total Fat (grams)	Carbs (grams)	Protein (grams)
Mixed	760	65	5	42
Carb	610	50	5	36
Protein	700	60	6	37

Coconut Kale with Sesame Crusted Salmon

6 servings

For the kale:

- 3   tablespoons olive oil
- 2 tablespoons minced fresh ginger
- 1 bunch kale, chopped
- 1½ cups coconut milk

    Salt and pepper to taste

1. Heat the oil in a large skillet. Add the ginger and sauté over medium heat for 5 minutes.

2. Add the kale, sauté, stirring constantly for 5 minutes.

3. Add the coconut milk and season with salt and pepper. Bring to a boil. Cover and reduce the heat, and simmer until kale is tender.

For the salmon:

- 6 salmon steaks (PT), or sole, perch, halibut etc. (CT)
- 4   tablespoons butter
- 4 tablespoons coconut oil
- 4 tablespoons minced ginger
- 1 cup sesame seeds

    Salt and freshly ground pepper, to taste

1. Preheat oven to 475°F.

2. In a small pan melt the butter and oil with the ginger.

Continued on page 167

3. Brush the butter, oil, and ginger on the pieces of salmon. Roll the salmon in the sesame seeds. Place the salmon on an oiled sheet pan and refrigerate for about 15 minutes.

4. Place the salmon in the oven and roast until the sesame seeds are brown and the salmon is rare inside, about 3 minutes. Season to taste with salt and pepper.

Recipe Type	Calories	Total Fat (grams)	Carbs (grams)	Protein (grams)
Mixed	568	53	16	16
Carb	572	52	16	19
Protein	565	54	16	16

Curried Halibut and Vegetables

4 servings

- 4   halibut steaks, 6 oz. each (CT), or 24 ounces scallops or shrimp (PT)
- ½   cup almond meal*
- 1   teaspoon salt
- 1   pinch cayenne
- 1   tablespoon curry powder
- 2   tablespoons olive oil
- 1   tablespoon coconut oil
- 3   tablespoons squeezed lemon

*Almond meal can be purchased at most grocery stores.

1. Mix the almond meal, salt, cayenne, and curry on a plate.

2. Flip the fish in the mix, coating both sides.

3. Heat the olive oil and coconut oil on medium heat in a frying pan. Add the fish to the pan and cook on each side about 5 minutes.

4. Remove from pan and serve with vegetables.

To prepare the vegetables:

- 1   head broccoli
- 1   head cauliflower
- ½   pound green beans
- 2   tablespoons coconut oil
- 1   tablespoon minced fresh ginger
- 1½   teaspoons cumin seeds
- ½   teaspoon black mustard seeds
- 1   teaspoon turmeric
  Chopped cilantro

Continued on page 169

1. Cut the broccoli and cauliflower into florets.

2. Heat the oil in large sauté pan. Add the ginger, cumin seeds, and mustard seeds, and sauté over low heat until the seeds "pop."

3. Add the broccoli, cauliflower, green beans, and turmeric to the pan. Add a sprinkle of salt and sauté over low heat. Stir frequently until all vegetables are tender.

4. Remove from heat and garnish with cilantro.

Recipe Type	Calories	Total Fat (grams)	Carbs (grams)	Protein (grams)
Mixed	574	38	26	40
Carb	642	49	25	35
Protein	506	28	27	37

Halibut Baked with Butter and Lemon

4 servings

> 2 pounds halibut fillet (CT), or salmon/scallops (PT)
> 1 lemon, juiced
> 1 tablespoon raw butter
> Salt and pepper to taste

1. Place the halibut in baking dish. Pour in lemon juice and add the butter, salt, and pepper.

2. Bake for 25–30 minutes on 350°F until fish is opaque.

3. Remove from oven and garnish with lemon slices.

Recipe Type	Calories	Total Fat (grams)	Carbs (grams)	Protein (grams)
Mixed	427	29	2	40
Carb	447	35	2	32
Protein	408	22	2	47

Salmon Supreme (PT)

4 servings

- 2 pounds wild Alaskan salmon
- 2 tablespoons extra virgin olive oil
- 1 tablespoon paprika
- 1 tablespoon Old Bay seasoning*
  Freshly ground black pepper
  Pinch of grey salt

1. Preheat oven to 400°F.

2. Rinse and pat dry salmon. Place on baking sheet and brush olive oil on both sides. Place skin side down and sprinkle the paprika and Old Bay seasoning on top. Grind a few good turns of black pepper and sprinkle a scant amount of gray salt.

3. Bake for 12 minutes. Remove from oven and cover with foil. Let stand for about 5 to 10 minutes. The salmon will continue to cook while resting. Cut into 4 pieces and serve.

NOTE: If Old Bay Seasoning is not available, another seafood seasoning would be fine, or a combination of celery salt, dried mustard, black pepper, and a small amount of the following: ground bay leaves, ground cloves, allspice, ginger, mace, cardamom, cinnamon, and paprika.

Recipe Type	Calories	Total Fat (grams)	Carbs (grams)	Protein (grams)
Protein	455	27	3	49

Fish Curry

4 servings

- 4 pieces (16 ounces) white fish of your choice, skinned and boned (CT), or salmon (PT)
- 1 onion, sliced
- 1 tomato, chopped
- 1 green chili, deseeded and chopped
- 1 cup coconut milk
- 1 tablespoon olive oil

Curry paste:

- 6 dry red chilies
- 1 tablespoon coriander seeds
- ½ tablespoon cumin seeds
- ½ tablespoon minced ginger
- ½ teaspoon minced garlic
- ½ tablespoon tamarind paste*
- 2 tablespoons water
- ½ teaspoon turmeric powder
- 5 tablespoons water or as required

1. Make paste by grinding all curry paste ingredients together until well blended. Set aside.

2. Rub the fish slices with some salt and a pinch of turmeric powder. Set aside for 5 minutes. Rinse well and drain.

3. Heat oil in heavy pan. Sauté onions over medium heat for about 5 minutes or till the onions are golden brown.

Continued on page 173

4. Add the curry paste and tomatoes. Sauté for 2–3 minutes.

5. Add the coconut milk and water. Bring to boil. Add the fish, green chilies and salt. Mix gently and simmer on low heat for about 4 minutes or till the fish is cooked.

6. Serve with brown rice.

Can be purchased at Asian market.

Recipe Type	Calories	Total Fat (grams)	Carbs (grams)	Protein (grams)
Mixed	410	26	14	30
Carb	350	23	14	25
Protein	380	25	14	29

White Fish and Garlic Stew

4 servings

- 2 tablespoons raw butter
- 3 tablespoons olive oil
- 2 medium onions, halved and sliced thinly
- 10 cloves garlic, minced
- ½ medium cauliflower, peeled and cubed (PT), or 1 medium green pepper, sliced (CT)
- 1 bunch Swiss chard, chopped
- 2½ pounds white fish
- 1 medium lemon, juiced
- 3 tablespoons flat leaf parsley, chopped
- Salt and pepper to taste

1. Melt the butter and 1 tablespoon olive oil in large stewing pot or dutch oven. Add the onions and garlic, cook over medium heat, stirring until softened, about 5 minutes.

2. Add the cauliflower or green pepper, season with salt and pepper, and cook, stirring gently until cauliflower/green pepper are about half cooked, 7–10 minutes. Add the chard and cook for another 3 minutes.

Continued on page 175

3. In the pot, place the fish over the vegetables, pour in the remaining 2 tablespoons olive oil, and add enough water to just about cover the fish. Season with salt and pepper. Simmer semi-covered over medium low heat until the fish is flakey and the liquid almost gone, about 20 minutes. Adjust the seasoning and pour in the lemon juice. Garnish with chopped parsley. Serve hot.

Note: Serve over quinoa or brown rice.

Recipe Type	Calories	Total Fat (grams)	Carbs (grams)	Protein (grams)
Mixed	509	20	14	70
Carb	505	19	13	70
Protein	514	20	14	71

Sautéed Salmon with Pesto

4 servings

- 2 pounds salmon, skinned and boned (PT), or snapper or tilapia (CT)
- 4 tablespoons lime juice
- 2 tablespoons tamari
- 1 teaspoon coconut oil

Pesto:

- 2 bunches basil or cilantro
- 2 tablespoons pine nuts
- 2 teaspoons miso paste
- 2 cloves garlic, sliced
- 5 tablespoons olive oil

1. Marinate the salmon in the lime juice and tamari for 30 minutes to 1 hour. Remove from the marinade and pat dry.

2. Heat skillet and place the coconut oil in the skillet. When melted add salmon and cook both sides for about 3–4 minutes each.

3. Place all the ingredients for the pesto in a food processor and blend till creamy. Serve the salmon topped with pesto sauce, with brown rice and a salad or vegetable of your choice.

Recipe Type	Calories	Total Fat (grams)	Carbs (grams)	Protein (grams)
Mixed	546	35	10	49
Carb	467	26	10	47
Protein	626	42	10	50

Organ and Raw Meat

Beef Carpaccio (PT)

4 servings

- 1 pound grass-fed beef tenderloin (PT)
- 4 cups fresh arugula (CT), or spinach (PT)
- ⅓ cup extra virgin olive oil
  Sea salt and freshly ground black pepper
  Small wedge of Parmesan cheese
- 1 lemon, cut into 4 wedges

1. Freeze beef tenderloin for 2 hours. Remove from freezer and slice thinly, into about ⅛-inch thick pieces. Cover with a sheet of plastic wrap and pound with a meat mallet until paper-thin.

2. Place 1 cup each arugula on 4 chilled individual plates. Top with equal amounts of sliced beef. Drizzle with the olive oil, and season with the salt and pepper. Top with shaved Parmesan cheese, and serve with a lemon wedge.

Recipe Type	Calories	Total Fat (grams)	Carbs (grams)	Protein (grams)
Protein	424	35	4	24

Beef Liver with Mushrooms (PT)

⅓ cup flour

½ teaspoon sea salt

¼ teaspoon freshly ground pepper

1 pound beef liver, cut in strips

3 tablespoons olive oil

1 cup sliced mushrooms

½ cup sliced scallions

½ cup sliced celery

1 cup chicken broth

1. Combine flour, salt and pepper together in a shallow dish. Add liver to coat all sides.

2. Heat 2 tablespoons oil in a large skillet on medium high heat. Add liver and cook until just browned. Add mushrooms, scallions, celery, and the remaining 1 tablespoon of oil. Cook, stirring frequently for about 5 minutes, or until vegetables are tender.

3. Stir in broth. Continue to cook about 5 minutes. Serve hot.

Recipe Type	Calories	Total Fat (grams)	Carbs (grams)	Protein (grams)
Protein	277	15	13	23

Steak Tartare (PT)

4 servings

- 1 pound organic, grass fed Filet Mignon, freshly ground (butcher can do this)*
- ¼ cup dry red wine
- 1 tablespoon Dijon mustard
- 3 cloves garlic, minced
- 1 teaspoon hot sauce
- 2 teaspoons dry mustard
- 1 teaspoon salt
- 4 tablespoons capers, drained
- 1 medium red onion, sliced thinly

1. In a large bowl combine the ground steak, wine, mustard, garlic, hot sauce, dry mustard and salt. Gently toss, being careful to not pack the meat together too much. Cover and refrigerate for 2 hours.

2. Mound on four chilled plates and garnish each with 1 tablespoon of capers and a few red onion slices (or to taste).

*Because this beef is served raw, we recommend using Filet Mignon. A high quality, low-fat beef has a lesser chance of contamination.

Recipe Type	Calories	Total Fat (grams)	Carbs (grams)	Protein (grams)
Protein	322	22	5	23

Beef Tongue with Garlic and Green Beans (PT)

6 servings

2 cups beef stock
¼ cup tamari soy sauce
4 cloves of garlic, sliced
2 inch piece of fresh ginger, sliced
¼ teaspoon ground cloves
1 teaspoon sea salt
½ teaspoon freshly ground pepper
3 pounds beef tongue
3 stalks celery, sliced
1 cup sliced mushrooms
1 cup green beans, trimmed and cut into 1 inch pieces
¼ cup cold water
2 tablespoons arrowroot

1. In a large stock pot over high heat combine the stock, tamari, garlic, ginger, cloves, salt, and pepper. Stir and add the beef tongue. Bring to a boil, reduce heat and cover. Simmer for 2 hours. Tongue should be tender.

2. Remove tongue from pan and remove the skin. Return to pot and add the celery, mushrooms and green beans. Return to a boil, reduce heat and cover. Simmer for about 10 minutes, or until vegetables are crisp-tender. Remove vegetables and tongue from the pan. Set aside and keep warm.

Continued on page 183

3. To make gravy, skim fat from the liquid. If the liquid is low, add more beef stock so the liquid equals 1½ cups. In a small bowl combine the cold water with the arrowroot until arrowroot dissolves fully. Add to the liquid in the pan and stir. Cook over medium high heat, stirring constantly, until thickened. Continue to cook for 2–3 more minutes.

4. Slice the tongue thinly and serve with the cooked vegetables and gravy.

Note: Some may be turned off by eating cow tongue but this truly is a delicacy in many parts of the world and tastes delicious.

Recipe Type	Calories	Total Fat (grams)	Carbs (grams)	Protein (grams)
Protein	546	36	15	38

Sweetbreads in Cream and Wine Sauce

4 servings

    1   pound sweetbreads (organ meats)
    2   quarts water
    2   tablespoons salt
    2   tablespoons fresh lemon juice
    2   tablespoons butter
    2   tablespoons arrowroot
 1¼   cup milk
  ½   teaspoon sea salt
       Freshly ground pepper, to taste
  ¼   cup dry white wine
  ¼   cup chopped flat-leaf parsley

1. Rinse the sweetbreads and place in a medium saucepan. Cover with about 2 quarts of water; add 2 tablespoons salt and 2 tablespoons lemon juice. Bring to a boil, and cook for 25 minutes. Drain liquid and set meat aside to cool. Once cool enough to handle, pull the outer membranes from the meat.

2. In a medium saucepan over medium low melt the butter. Add arrowroot and whisk in until combined into a paste-like consistency. Add milk and stir constantly until mixture is thick and bubbly. Add salt and pepper and cook gently 2 minutes.

3. Add sweetbreads and cook until reheated, about 5 to 10 minutes. Add wine, stir and serve. Garnish each serving with 1 tablespoon of parsley.

Recipe Type	Calories	Total Fat (grams)	Carbs (grams)	Protein (grams)
Mixed	288	20	5	20

Healthy Recipes for Your Nutritional Type

Eggs

Mushroom and Broccoli Frittata

4 servings

- 6 eggs
- 2 cups broccoli (CT), or cauliflower (PT), steamed and chopped
- 4 medium potatoes, steamed and chopped
- 1 small onion, chopped
- 6 medium mushrooms, sliced
- 1 tablespoon olive oil
- 1 cup cheese (your choice), grated

1. Steam the potatoes and broccoli. Set aside.

2. Sauté the onions and mushrooms. Set aside.

3. Beat the eggs well and mix them together in a large bowl with the potatoes, broccoli, onions and mushrooms. Add to a skillet with a metal handle.

4. Cook over medium to low heat for about 15 minutes until the frittata is cooked but still a little moist in the middle.

5. Place grated cheese on top and put under the broiler till cheese browns lightly. Let it cool a little and serve.

Recipe Type	Calories	Total Fat (grams)	Carbs (grams)	Protein (grams)
Mixed	435	19	41	26
Carb	436	19	41	26
Protein	434	19	41	26

Mushroom and Spinach Quiche

4 servings

Pastry:
- 1½   cups spelt four
- ½   cup butter
- 3   tablespoons cold water

Filling:
- 6   medium eggs, whisked
- 2   cups warm milk
- ½   teaspoon salt
- ¾   cup grated Gruyere cheese
- ½   pound spinach, chopped (PT), or green peppers (CT)
- 10   medium mushrooms, chopped (PT), or onions (CT)

1. Place the flour and butter in food processor and blend till pea sized pieces are formed. Add water slowly till dough forms thick ball. Touch as little as possible. Put in refrigerator for 30 minutes. Preheat oven to 350°F.

2. Roll out dough into pan. Poke small holes in the dough with a fork to prevent it from causing bubbles while cooking. Place in oven for 20 minutes, then remove and fill.

3. Combine eggs, milk, salt, pepper, and half the cheese. Add the vegetables and place the rest of the cheese on top.

4. Dot the top of the quiche with extra butter if you do not want a skin to form.

5. Place in oven for 30 minutes or until set. Remove when the outside is set and the middle still moves a little. Let stand for 10–15 minutes before serving.

Recipe Type	Calories	Total Fat (grams)	Carbs (grams)	Protein (grams)
Mixed	687	42	56	24
Carb	746	42	71	25
Protein	629	42	42	23

Nori and Eggs

4–6 servings

1   tablespoon umeboshi vinegar
1   carrot, sliced into ¼" strips
1   tablespoon toasted sesame oil
2   cups spinach leaves (PT), or kale (CT)
2   cups water
3   tablespoon tamari soy sauce
2   eggs
¼   cup vegetable water, reserved from spinach water
4   sheets nori
1   teaspoon fresh lemon juice

1. Sauté carrot strips in oil over low heat until soft. Let cool.

2. Steam spinach until soft. Strain and keep water. Cool and squeeze into a long flat shape. Slice into long strips. Top with 1 table-spoon tamari.

3. Whisk the eggs, remaining tamari and ¼ cup spinach water. Pour egg mixture over medium heat. Cook eggs as an omelet, fold-ing over 4 times, into a long strip. Cool and slice lengthwise.

4. Toast a nori sheet over a low flame or toast in toaster, both sides, until greenish color. Place nori on sushi mat or flat surface. About ½" from bottom, place carrot strips, spinach, and omelet across it.

5. Roll the nori and vegetables on the sushi mat (or flat surface), keeping it firm, even, and smooth. Using finger, wet the edges with lemon juice to seal the nori.

6. Serve in cut pieces or eat as a wrap.

Recipe Type	Calories	Total Fat (grams)	Carbs (grams)	Protein (grams)
Mixed	63	4	3	4
Carb	67	4	7	4
Protein	58	4	2	4

Soft Boiled Eggs with Dulse and Nutritional Yeast

4 servings

- 8 medium eggs
- 2 teaspoons nutritional yeast*
- 2 teaspoons dulse flakes*
- 2 teaspoons raw butter, melted

  Salt and pepper

1. Place eggs in a pan of cold water. Place on high heat. Bring to boil, and cook for 4–6 minutes, depending on how hard or soft you want the eggs to be.

2. Remove shells. Place 2 eggs in each of 4 bowls, slice in half and put half a teaspoon of melted butter on each serving.

3. Sprinkle with yeast and dulse. Serve.

Note: Serve with steamed veggies or salad.

*Can be found at local health food store or online.

Recipe Type	Calories	Total Fat (grams)	Carbs (grams)	Protein (grams)
Mixed	158	11	2	12

Zucchini Egg Omelet with Mushrooms

1 serving

- 2 organic free range eggs
- 1 tablespoon water
- ⅛ teaspoon sea salt
- Freshly ground pepper
- 1 tablespoon ghee, or butter
- ⅛ cup crumbled goat cheese

Zucchini and Mushroom:

- ½ cup sliced zucchini
- ½ cup sliced button mushrooms
- 1 cup spinach (PT), or ½ diced onions and bell peppers (CT)
- 1 tablespoon ghee, or butter

1. In a skillet melt ghee. Add sliced zucchini, mushrooms, and spinach (or onions and peppers). Cook until tender but not brown. Set aside.

2. In a bowl combine eggs, water, salt, and a grind of pepper. Using a whisk, beat until combined but not frothy. In an 8- or 10-inch skillet with flared sides, heat ghee. Lift and tilt the pan to coat the sides.

3. Add egg mixture to skillet; cook over medium heat. As eggs set, run a spatula around the edge of the skillet, lifting eggs and letting uncooked portion flow underneath. When eggs are set but still shiny, spoon filling of zucchini and mushrooms across center of omelet. Sprinkle crumbled goat cheese atop filling. Fold omelet in half. Transfer onto a warm plate.

Recipe Type	Calories	Total Fat (grams)	Carbs (grams)	Protein (grams)
Mixed	464	39	13	20
Carb	479	39	17	20
Protein	449	39	9	20

Recipes for Your Nutritional Type

Vegetarian and Legume Main Dishes

Arame and Lentils

1 cup brown lentils, rinsed well
1 bay leaf
¼ cup arame, (seaweed)
¼ cup toasted sesame seeds
2 tablespoons minced parsley
1 carrot, shredded

1. Put the lentils in a saucepan, add the bay leaf, and cover with cold water. Bring to a boil, skim off any foam, cover and reduce heat to simmer. Simmer for 30 minutes or until lentils are tender.

2. Drain the water from the beans and discard the bay leaf. Set aside to cool.

3. When lentils are at room temperature, combine the remaining ingredients, mix well, and serve with red pepper sauce.

Red Pepper Sauce:

4 large red peppers
2 tablespoons lemon juice
1 jalapeno pepper, seeded
1 teaspoon dried basil
2 tablespoons olive oil
Pinch of cayenne

1. Roast red peppers under a broiler until browned.

2. Let rest in a bowl for 10 minutes. Peel skins, remove stems and seeds. Rinse.

3. Blend the red peppers with the remaining ingredients in a blender.

CT: Lentils are better for PT's but CT's can have them occasionally.

Recipe Type	Calories	Total Fat (grams)	Carbs (grams)	Protein (grams)
Protein	337	14	43	18

Recipes for Your Nutritional Type

Chickpea Stew

4 servings

2 tablespoons extra virgin olive oil

1 medium yellow onion, finely sliced

4 cloves garlic, finely minced

1 teaspoon chili powder

1 teaspoon salt

1 teaspoon paprika

1 28-ounce can crushed tomatoes

2 14-ounce cans chickpeas (garbanzo beans), drained and rinsed

2 cups baby spinach leaves (PT), or 2 cups chard (CT)

1 tablespoon lemon juice

1. Heat oil in a medium saucepan over medium heat. Add onion and garlic to pan; cook, stirring frequently, until onions are soft.

2. Add the chili powder, salt, and paprika. Stir for 1 minute.

3. Add undrained tomatoes and chickpeas, stir until combined. Bring to a boil, reduce heat and simmer 10 minutes, until flavors blend and chickpeas are tender. Stir in spinach (or chard) in handfuls until wilted.

4. Remove from heat. Stir in lemon juice and serve.

PT: For a full meal, stir in cooked, diced and warm dark meat chicken before serving.

Recipe Type	Calories	Total Fat (grams)	Carbs (grams)	Protein (grams)
Mixed	539	14	84	25
Carb	546	14	86	25
Protein	532	14	83	24

Mighty Mushrooms and Beans

4 servings

- 2 tablespoons olive oil
- 4 tablespoons coconut oil or butter
- 2 shallots, chopped
- 3 garlic cloves, crushed
- 1½ pounds mixed mushrooms (chanterelle, shiitake, maitake) (PT), or broccoli (CT)
- 4 pieces of sun-dried tomatoes in oil, drained and chopped
- 6 tablespoons white wine
- 1 15-ounce can of red kidney or pinto beans, drained (PT), or half can beans (CT)
- 3 tablespoons Parmesan cheese, grated (optional)
- 2 tablespoons fresh parsley, chopped
  Salt and black pepper

1. Heat the oil and butter in a frying pan, add shallots, and sauté until soft.

2. Add the garlic and mushrooms to the pan and sauté for 3–4 minutes.

3. Stir in the sun-dried tomatoes, and wine. Add salt and pepper to taste.

4. Stir in the beans and cook for about 5–6 minutes, until most of the liquid has evaporated and the beans are soft.

5. Stir in the cheese. Remove from heat and sprinkle with parsley.

Recipe Type	Calories	Total Fat (grams)	Carbs (grams)	Protein (grams)
Mixed	463	23	51	18
Carb	425	23	39	18
Protein	500	23	62	17

Lentil, Wild Rice and Root Vegetable Roulades with Orange-Ginger Sauce

4 servings

½ cup dried lentils

1½ cups vegetable stock

Bouquet garni (ingredients and instructions follows)

Salt and pepper, to taste

1 tablespoon olive oil

2 leeks, washed and cut into ½ inch dice

4 cloves garlic, minced

¼ cup vegetable stock

2 parsnips, cut into ½ inch dice

1 small butternut squash, cut into ½ inch dice

1 small celery root bulb, peeled and cut into ½ inch dice, or 1 cup of sliced fennel, or 1 cup of sliced celery

1 tablespoon fresh thyme

1 tablespoon fresh marjoram

1 tablespoon fresh sage

½ teaspoon ground nutmeg

½ cup vegetable stock

1½ cups cooked wild rice (about ½ cup uncooked)

1 package filo dough, thawed

Olive oil for brushing filo

1. To assemble bouquet garni put 1 bay leaf, 1 teaspoon black peppercorns, 3–4 fresh sprigs of thyme, marjoram and sage together in a bundle using cheesecloth and tie closed. This allows the herbs and seasoning to add flavor without leaving small bits in the lentils.

Continued on page 199

2. In a medium saucepan with a tight-fitting lid, combine lentils, stock, and bouquet garni and bring to a gentle boil. Lower heat, cover, and simmer until lentils are tender but not mushy, about 30 minutes. Remove from heat, drain, remove and discard bouquet garni, and season with salt and pepper to taste. Set aside to cool.

3. In a large saucepan, heat olive oil over medium heat. Cook the leeks, garlic, and stock until the vegetables are softened, about 10 minutes. Add the parsnips, turnips, squash, celery root, thyme, marjoram, sage, nutmeg, salt, and stock. Cover and simmer until the root vegetables are just tender, about 15 minutes. Remove from heat, stir in the wild rice and lentils, and let cool.

4. To assemble: Preheat the oven to 350°F. Remove 2 filo sheets and place them on a flat work surface. Place a damp towel over the remaining filo to keep it moist. Brush the two sheets with olive oil, then cover with 2 more sheets and brush with oil again.

5. Spread the filling on the bottom third of the filo stack in a bed about 2 inches deep and 2 inches thick. Starting at the bottom, roll the stack into a tight cylinder. Cut it into four portions, transfer them to a baking sheet, and bake for 20 minutes, or until crust is golden.

6. When done, slice each roulade in half diagonally so each piece of filo looks like a triangle. Place two filo triangles in the center of the plate. Pour a large spoonful of Orange-Ginger Sauce (recipe follows) over the roulades and sprinkle a garnish of fresh herbs.

Note: For a wheat-free substitution, you can use brown rice lasagna noodles instead of filo dough.

Orange-Ginger Sauce continued on 200

continued from 199

Orange-Ginger Sauce:

- 2 cups orange juice (5–6 oranges)
- 1 tablespoon freshly grated ginger root
- 1 tablespoon unrefined coconut oil
- 1 tablespoon honey
  Pinch of fresh thyme
- 4 teaspoons kudzu, or arrowroot (corn and wheat-free thickeners), dissolved in 2 tablespoons cold water
- 1½ teaspoons tamari soy sauce

1. In a small saucepan, heat all the ingredients except the dissolved kudzu. Bring to a boil and then whisk in the kudzu mix. Cook for another minute. Serve hot.

PT: Add meat of choice to filling

Recipe Type	Calories	Total Fat (grams)	Carbs (grams)	Protein (grams)
Mixed	412	9	77	13

Zucchini Latkes

4–6 servings

- 4 cups grated zucchini
- 1 head cauliflower
- 1 medium onion, thinly sliced
- 4 eggs
- 3 tablespoons mint, chopped
- 1 tablespoon sea salt
- 1 tablespoon black pepper
- 2 tablespoons butter
- 2 tablespoons coconut oil
- ½ cup raw yogurt

1. Mix the zucchini in a bowl with the salt and let stand for 1 hour. Rinse well, place zucchini in a tea towel (or clean cloth) and wring out the water.

2. Cut the cauliflower into florets and steam until soft. Drain, cool, and mash.

3. Squeeze as much liquid as possible from the cauliflower with the tea towel.

4. Heat the butter and 1 tablespoon oil in a medium size frying pan over low heat. Add the onions and cook for about 5–10 minutes.

5. Combine the zucchini, cauliflower, and onions in a bowl. Add the eggs and mint. Season with salt and pepper. Mix well.

6. Over medium heat, add remaining tablespoon of olive oil to pan. Spoon out individual patties and cook until browned on each side, about 8 minutes. Serve with a dollop of yogurt.

Recipe Type	Calories	Total Fat (grams)	Carbs (grams)	Protein (grams)
Mixed	181	13	11	9

Recipes for Your Nutritional Type

Spaghetti Squash with Wicked Good Sauce (CT)

4 servings

    1 spaghetti squash, about 3 pounds
  ¾-1 cup wicked good sauce (recipe follows)

1. Preheat oven to 350°F. Rinse squash, poke with fork or metal skewer in about six places, and place in shallow baking pan with sides.

2. Bake for 90 minutes or until fork tender. Allow squash to cool about 10 minutes, then transfer to cutting board. Cut in half lengthwise. Remove seeds and pulp with a large spoon or an ice cream scoop; discard. Using a fork, rake flesh onto a large platter or bowl to create spaghetti-like strands.

3. Toss the squash with Wicked Good Sauce. Serve warm.

Wicked Good Sauce:

    ¼ medium-sized onion, chopped
    1 teaspoon extra virgin olive oil
    1 clove garlic
    ½ teaspoon minced ginger
    ¼ green bell pepper
    1 tablespoon almond butter
    1 tablespoon tamari soy sauce
    ½ cup water (or more)
    2 tablespoons chopped celery leaves
    2 Tablespoons Toasted Pumpkin Seeds

Continued on page 203

Healthy Recipes for Your Nutritional Type

1. Sauté onion in oil with the whole garlic. When the onion is tender, smash the garlic with a fork. Add the ginger and bell pepper and cook gently a minute more.

2. Stir in the almond butter and tamari, and then add the water and celery leaves. Stir until smooth; then simmer about 5 minutes. Add the pumpkin seeds and heat through.

Recipe Type	Calories	Total Fat (grams)	Carbs (grams)	Protein (grams)
Carb	153	6	26	4

Stuffed Portobello's
With Lemon, Thyme and Aduki Beans

4–6 servings

- 1 cup dried aduki beans, or 2 cups canned
- 3 tablespoons olive oil
- 1 medium onion, finely chopped
- 2 garlic cloves, crushed
- 2 tablespoons fresh thyme, chopped
- 8 large portobello mushrooms, stalks removed and chopped
- 1 cup spelt bread crumbs (CT), or ¾ cup ground almonds or walnuts (PT)
- Juice of 1 lemon
- ¾ cup goat cheese, crumbled (optional)
- ¼ pound fresh spinach (PT), or kale (CT)

1. If using fresh beans, soak overnight, then drain and rinse well. Place in a saucepan, add enough water to cover and bring to a boil for 10 minutes. Reduce heat and cook for another 30 minutes until tender. Drain and set aside. If using canned, drain, rinse, and set aside.

2. Preheat oven to 400°F. Heat the olive oil in a large frying pan. Add the onion and garlic. Sauté until onions are soft.

3. Add the thyme and mushroom stalks, cook for 3 minutes more, stirring occasionally.

4. Stir in the beans, bread crumbs, and lemon juice. Add salt and pepper to taste and cook for 2 minutes until heated through.

5. Mash about two-thirds of the beans with a fork or potato - masher, leaving the remaining beans whole.

Continued on page 205

6. Brush a baking dish and the base and sides of the mushroom tops with olive oil. Then fill each mushroom with a spoonful of bean mixture. Place mushrooms in the baking dish, cover with foil, and bake for 20 minutes.

7. Remove the foil. Top each mushroom with some of the goat cheese and bake for another 15 minutes or until the cheese is bubbly and mushrooms are tender.

8. Serve with a bed of steamed spinach (PT), or steamed kale (CT).

Recipe Type	Calories	Total Fat (grams)	Carbs (grams)	Protein (grams)
Mixed	516	21	72	14
Carb	474	14	76	13
Protein	560	27	67	16

Vegetable Parmesan Gratin

8 servings

- 1 cup broccoli, cut into florets (CT), or asparagus, cut into 1-inch pieces (PT)
- 1 cup cauliflower, cut into florets
- 1 zucchini, sliced thin
- 1 celery stalk, sliced thin
- 1 cup mushrooms, sliced thin
- 2 whole green onions, sliced thin
- 2 tablespoons chopped fresh dill
- 4 large eggs
- 2½ cups grated Parmesan cheese
- ¼ cup olive oil
- ¼ teaspoon salt
- ¼ teaspoon pepper
- 2 cups bread crumbs
  Additional salt and pepper, to taste

1. Preheat the oven to 350°F.

2. Steam the broccoli, cauliflower, zucchini and celery until just tender, about 5 minutes. Place in a colander and run under cold water to stop the cooking. Set aside.

3. Combine the uncooked mushrooms, green onions, and dill in a bowl.

Continued on page 207

4. In a small bowl beat the eggs until blended. Whisk in the Parmesan cheese, olive oil, and salt and pepper.

5. In an oiled shallow casserole dish arrange a layer of steamed vegetables, then a layer of the uncooked vegetable mixture, and a layer of the egg-cheese mixture. Continue to layer until all ingredients are used. Cover with bread crumbs and a little more salt and pepper. Bake until set and firm, and the bread crumbs are browned, about 40 minutes.

Recipe Type	Calories	Total Fat (grams)	Carbs (grams)	Protein (grams)
Mixed	362	19	27	21
Carb	363	19	27	21
Protein	362	19	27	21

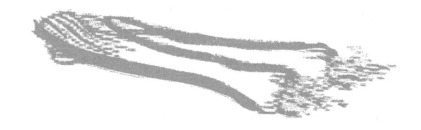

Warmed Greek Lentils with Feta and Dill

5 servings

- 1¼ cups dried green lentils, rinsed well
- 3 cloves of garlic
- 3 bay leaves
- 3 medium carrots, peeled, and finely diced
- 1 teaspoon salt
- ¼ cup olive oil
- 2 tablespoons fresh lemon juice
- 1 medium celery stalk, diced finely
- 3 medium radishes, diced finely
- 2 tablespoons fresh dill, minced
- 8 cups mesclun salad mix (CT), or spinach (PT)
- 5 ounces feta cheese, crumbled (optional)

1. In a medium saucepan, bring lentils, garlic cloves, bay leaves, and 2 quarts of water to boil.

2. Reduce heat and simmer for 15 minutes.

3. Stir in carrots and 1 teaspoon salt. Continue cooking until carrots and lentils are tender (not mushy), about 10 minutes.

4. Drain and discard the bay leaves and garlic.

5. Meanwhile, whisk the olive oil, lemon juice, and salt to taste, together in a bowl.

Continued on page 209

Healthy Recipes for Your Nutritional Type

6. Add the lentils, celery, radishes, and dill to the lemon juice mixture.

7. Toss and combine, adjusting taste adding salt and pepper. Allow the lentil salad to cool for 10 minutes.

8. Sprinkle with feta cheese and serve.

Recipe Type	Calories	Total Fat (grams)	Carbs (grams)	Protein (grams)
Mixed	224	17	12	8
Carb	225	17	13	8
Protein	224	17	12	8

Sandwiches

Rye Crisp "Sandwich"
with Avocado, Sprouts and Sheep's Cheese

4 servings

- 8   rye crisp crackers
- 4   tablespoons Dijon mustard
- 8   slices Grass-Fed Cheddar Cheese, or other raw or grass-fed cheese of choice
- 1   avocado, sliced
- ¼   cup broccoli sprouts
      Fresh lemon juice, to taste

1. Spread each rye crisp cracker with ½ tablespoon mustard. Place one slice of cheese on each cracker. Then lay 2 or 3 slices of avocado on top on the cheese. Top each with a tablespoon of sprouts. Sprinkle each with a squeeze of fresh lemon juice.

PT: Reduce or replace avocado with roast beef slices.

CT: Use a low-fat cheese or cucumber slices.

Note: For a low-carb, wheat-free substitution, you can use nori sheets or cabbage leaves instead of crackers.

Recipe Type	Calories	Total Fat (grams)	Carbs (grams)	Protein (grams)
Mixed	423	25	40	16
Carb	270	12	40	6
Protein	377	20	33	20

Chicken Burgers with Red Peppers

6 servings

  2 tablespoons olive oil
  1 medium onion, diced small
  3 cloves garlic, minced
  2 tablespoons ginger, minced
  2 tablespoons tamari
  1 tablespoon toasted sesame oil
  1 red pepper, diced small
  3 scallions, minced
  ½ cup fresh basil, minced
 1½ pounds ground chicken, dark meat
  1 large egg white, lightly beaten
 1½ tablespoons olive oil

1. Heat olive oil in a medium skillet. Add onion, garlic and ginger and sauté over medium heat for about 5 minutes. Season with tamari and toasted sesame oil, stir and remove from heat. Place in a bowl to cool. Set aside.

2. Prepare pepper, scallion, and cilantro as directed and add to the bowl.

3. Crumble ground chicken into the bowl and add egg white. Using your hands mix gently to combine. Shape into 1/2 inch thick patties about 3 inches in diameter.

Continued on page 215

4. Place a heavy skillet over medium high heat and add olive oil. Add patties and cook for about 3–5 minutes on each side, turning only once. Do not press.

5. Check for doneness by inserting the tip of a paring knife into the center of one of the patties. The center should not be pink and the juices should run clear. Serve on a bun with pea shoots and teriyaki mustard.

Recipe Type	Calories	Total Fat (grams)	Carbs (grams)	Protein (grams)
Mixed	361	25	6	28

Eggplant Sandwich (CT)

4 servings

- 3 medium eggplants
- 2 tablespoons coconut oil
  Sea salt and freshly ground pepper
- 2 yellow bell peppers
- 12 sun-dried tomatoes
- 8 ounces of goat cheese
- 16 small basil leaves

1. Cut each eggplant lengthwise into slices about ½ inch thick. Take the largest eight slices and place on a baking pan. Sprinkle with salt and let sit for 20 minutes.

2. Thoroughly rinse the eggplant slices and pat dry.

3. Heat a large skillet over medium heat. Add the coconut oil and heat until glistening. Add the eggplant slices 2 at a time. Cook until browned, about 3 minutes per side. Remove from pan and set aside to drain on paper towels. Sprinkle with salt and pepper.

4. Roast the bell peppers on the grill, or on a grill pan, preheated on high. Arrange whole peppers on the grill and cook until the skin is charred, about 5 minutes per side. Place the hot peppers in a paper bag. This allows the skin to be removed easily. Allow to cool in the bag for about 20 minutes. Pull or scrape the skin off with your fingers or a paring knife. Cut off the stem end, cut open the peppers and scrape out the seeds and membrane. Cut into strips about 1 inch wide.

continued on 217

5. Cut the sun-dried tomatoes into strips.

6. Assemble the sandwiches by placing an eggplant slice on a plate. Spread each slice with goat cheese and top as desired with slices of roasted peppers, sun-dried tomatoes, and basil leaves. To complete the sandwich place another eggplant slice on top.

Recipe Type	Calories	Total Fat (grams)	Carbs (grams)	Protein (grams)
Carb	351	20	33	17

Portobello Sandwich

4 servings

8 portobello mushroom caps, grilled
¼ cup plain yogurt (PT), or low-fat plain yogurt (CT)
¼ cup almond butter (PT)
1 large tomato, sliced
4 romaine lettuce leaves
1 avocado, sliced
1 cup alfalfa sprouts
½ medium red onion, sliced thinly
¼ cup toasted sunflower seeds (PT)

1. Spread almond butter on the underside of each mushroom cap. Top with a layer of yogurt.

2. Add slices of tomato, avocado, and onion as desired. Top with alfalfa sprouts and sunflower seeds. Place a lettuce leaf on top and cover with another mushroom cap.

3. Serve and eat like a sandwich.

Recipe Type	Calories	Total Fat (grams)	Carbs (grams)	Protein (grams)
Mixed	231	17	19	6
Carb	139	8	16	4
Protein	289	23	21	8

Tempeh Reuben

6 servings

- 2 packages tempeh, crumbled
- 3 tablespoons tamari soy sauce
- 3 tablespoons Dijon mustard
- 1 tablespoon olive oil
- 1 medium yellow onion, sliced thin
- 24 ounces raw sauerkraut
  Sea salt, to taste
- 6 large romaine lettuce leaves, whole

1. Crumble the tempeh and place in a steamer basket. Steam for 20 minutes. Remove and place in a medium bowl.

2. Whisk together the tamari and mustard. Pour over the steamed tempeh, and stir to combine. Cover the bowl with a plate and allow to sit while preparing the remaining ingredients.

3. Heat oil in a large skillet over medium high heat. When oil shimmers, add the onions. Sauté until onions are brown, about 10 minutes. Turn off heat, but let pan stay on burner.

4. Add the steamed tempeh mixture and sauerkraut to the pan, stir to combine. Allow to stay on burner, covered, until heated through. Season to taste with salt.

5. Serve in lettuce leaves.

Note: Both CT and PT can have tempeh.

Recipe Type	Calories	Total Fat (grams)	Carbs (grams)	Protein (grams)
Mixed	222	12	16	18

Baked Goods

Banana Muffins

12 muffins

- 1¼ cups rice flour
- ¼ teaspoon salt
- 1½ teaspoons baking powder
- ¼ cup walnuts, toasted and chopped
- 2 sticks unsalted butter, softened
- ⅓ cup honey
- 1½ cups mashed bananas
- 2 eggs, whipped

1. Preheat the oven to 350°F. Place walnuts in a single layer on a baking sheet and cook in oven for 10 minutes. Remove from oven, set aside to cool. When cool enough to handle, chop.

2. In a medium bowl, combine the flour, salt, baking powder, and walnuts.

3. In a small bowl, combine the butter and honey until creamed. Add the bananas and whipped eggs.

4. Add the butter and banana mixture to the flour mixture and gently mix. Spoon into oiled muffin tins.

5. Bake for 35–40 minutes.

Recipe Type	Calories	Total Fat (grams)	Carbs (grams)	Protein (grams)
Mixed	270	18	26	3

Blueberry Walnut Muffins

Makes 22 muffins

- 2 cups spelt flour
- 2 cups oatmeal
- ½ cup sugar
- 1 tablespoon baking powder
- 1 teaspoon baking soda
- 1 teaspoon salt
- 11 tablespoons butter
- 1 cup blueberries (frozen or fresh)
- 1 cup walnuts (soaked overnight and dehydrated), chopped
- 1½ cups apple butter

1. Preheat oven to 375°F.

2. Mix dry ingredients, sift. Use your hands to cut in the butter, by rubbing flour and butter together until very small rice-like pieces are formed. Fold in blueberries and walnuts, then add the apple butter and mix well.

3. Pour into lightly oiled muffin tins. Bake for 15–20 minutes.

Recipe Type	Calories	Total Fat (grams)	Carbs (grams)	Protein (grams)
Mixed	201	10	28	2

Flourless Almond Torte

8 servings

- 1½ cups raw almonds
- ¼ cup maple syrup
- 3 eggs
- 1 teaspoon almond extract
- ½ teaspoon vanilla extract
- ¼ teaspoon sea salt
- 1 tablespoon lemon zest
- 2 tablespoons unsweetened coconut flakes, toasted
- 2 tablespoons almonds, toasted and chopped

1. Preheat the oven to 375°F. Line an 8-inch pan with parchment paper; cut to fit the bottom.

2. Place almonds in a food processor and grind until the consistency of the almonds is like flour, about 4 minutes. If the mixture starts sticking to the sides, run a spatula around to loosen.

3. In a small bowl add the syrup, eggs, extracts and salt. Mix well to fully incorporate the eggs. With the food processor running, pour the egg mixture through the feed tube and continue to process until smooth. Add the lemon zest and coconut and pulse to combine.

4. Pour the batter into the pan and bake for 25–30 minutes. When the top is lightly golden brown and the center is just set, the torte is ready. If the top browns too quickly, tent with foil.

5. Remove from oven and allow to cool. Garnish with toasted almonds.

Recipe Type	Calories	Total Fat (grams)	Carbs (grams)	Protein (grams)
Mixed	303	23	18	10

Sesame Biscuits

8 biscuits

2½   cups whole wheat pastry flour

3   tablespoons sesame seeds

1   tablespoon baking powder

1   teaspoon sea salt

6   tablespoons butter

3   tablespoons honey

2   tablespoons coconut oil

1   cup milk

1. Preheat oven to 400°F. Lightly oil a baking sheet.

2. In a large bowl combine the flour, sesame seeds, baking powder, and salt. Cut in the butter.

3. In a small bowl combine the honey, oil and milk. Add to the flour mixture. Gently fold ingredients together to just barely combine.

4. Remove dough from bowl and place on a floured cutting board. Knead about 8 times.

5. Roll the dough out to about ⅔ inches thick. Cut out using a biscuit cutter, or round cookie cutter. Place on the baking sheet, biscuits should be touching. Bake for 10–15 minutes.

Recipe Type	Calories	Total Fat (grams)	Carbs (grams)	Protein (grams)
Mixed	322	16	40	7

Raw or Fermented Foods

Apple Energy Soup

6 servings

>   2 medium apples, cored and cut into 4 pieces
>   Juice of ½ medium lemon
>   2 cups spring mix (CT), or spinach (PT)
>   1 avocado, peeled and pit removed
>   1 cup fresh mint leaves
>   4 cups water
>   Sea salt, to taste

1. In a blender, combine apples, lemon juice, greens, avocado, mint, and 2 cups of the water. Blend until smooth, adding more water as necessary for desired consistency. Season to taste with salt.

Recipe Type	Calories	Total Fat (grams)	Carbs (grams)	Protein (grams)
Mixed	103	6	13	4
Carb	89	5	11	2
Protein	109	6	14	4

Curried Red Pepper Soup (CT)

4 servings

- 4 red peppers, seeded and chopped
- ½ cup tahini
  Juice of 1 small lemon
- 2 cloves garlic, minced
  Pinch of cayenne
- 1½ teaspoons curry
- 3 scallions, minced

1. Blend all ingredients except scallions in blender or food processor. Add enough water to make a smooth soup consistency.

2. Chill and garnish with scallions.

Recipe Type	Calories	Total Fat (grams)	Carbs (grams)	Protein (grams)
Carb	231	17	19	7

Daikon and Carrot Pickles

4 servings

 8 ounces carrots, peeled and julienned (CT), or 8 ounces celery, julienned (PT)

 8 ounces daikon, peeled and julienned

 1 teaspoon sea salt

 1½ cups water

 ¼ cup rice vinegar

 2 tablespoons sugar

1. Place the carrots and daikon in a colander, sprinkle with the salt, and toss. Place over a bowl and allow to sit for 30 minutes.

2. In a small saucepan, combine the water, vinegar, and sugar. Bring just to a boil and immediately remove from heat. Cool at room temperature.

3. Rinse the carrots and daikon. Using your hands, squeeze any excess liquid and pat with paper towels. Transfer to a mixing bowl. Add the vinegar mixture and stir gently.

4. Allow to stand at least one hour before serving. Can be served at room temperature or chilled.

Recipe Type	Calories	Total Fat (grams)	Carbs (grams)	Protein (grams)
Mixed	47	0	12	1
Carb	58	0	14	1
Protein	36	0	9	1

Kimchi

6 servings

- 4 cups water
- 4 tablespoons sea salt
- 1 head cabbage, shredded
- 1 cup diakon radish, grated (CT), or 1 cup asparagus, cut into 1 inch pieces (PT)
- 1 cup green beans, cut into 1 inch pieces (PT)
- 2 scallions, chopped
- 2 cloves garlic, minced
- 2 tablespoons fresh ginger, minced
- ½ teaspoon cayenne pepper

1. In a large bowl mix a brine of the water and salt. Mix well to thoroughly dissolve salt. Add the cabbage and diakon radish. Cover with a plate or other weight to keep the vegetables submerged. Soak for 12 hours.

2. Drain the brine from the vegetables, reserving the brine. Taste the vegetables for saltiness. If they are too salty, you can rinse the vegetables. If they are not salty enough, sprinkle with a little more salt (1 teaspoon at a time).

3. Combine the asparagus (PT), green beans (PT), scallions, garlic, ginger, and cayenne pepper. Add to the cabbage mixture.

4. Put the whole mix into a jar or crock. Pour the soaking liquid over the vegetables, making sure that they are completely submerged in liquid.

Continued on page 233

5. Cover loosely with a clean cloth and set aside for 3–7 days. Ideally the room temperature is around 70° F to help with the fermentation. If it is colder the fermentation takes longer.

6. Check the kimchi daily. Make sure the vegetables stay covered in brine. After 3–7 days the kimchi will taste ripe. Once this happens, place in glass jar in the refrigerator. It will keep for months.

Recipe Type	Calories	Total Fat (grams)	Carbs (grams)	Protein (grams)
Mixed	67	0	16	3
Carb	66	0	16	3
Protein	73	0	17	4

Minted Cucumber Soup (CT)

4 servings

- 4 cucumbers, peeled and chopped
- 2 shallots
- ¼ cup tahini
- ¼ cup fresh mint
- 2 scallions, minced

1. Blend all ingredients and add enough water to make soup thick. Chill in refrigerator for 1 hour. Garnish with scallions when serving.

Recipe Type	Calories	Total Fat (grams)	Carbs (grams)	Protein (grams)
Carb	137	9	12	5

Pickled Cucumbers with Ginger (CT)

4 servings

- 4 cucumbers, peeled
- ½ cup sea salt
- 1 cup brown rice vinegar
- 3 tablespoons sugar
- 1 teaspoon sea salt
- 1 teaspoon freshly ground black pepper
- 6 tablespoons sliced fresh ginger, peeled

1. Slice the cucumbers very thin. Place in large bowl and sprinkle ½ cup sea salt. Using your hands toss the salt throughout the cucumbers and lightly squeeze the slices as you toss. Cover and let sit at room temperature for 1 hour. The salt draws the water content out of the cucumbers.

2. Pour the cucumbers and liquid into a colander to drain. While in the colander use your hands to squish out as much water as possible. Return cucumbers to bowl.

3. Add the vinegar, sugar, salt, pepper, and ginger. Toss to combine. Cover and refrigerate 12–24 hours.

4. Remove from refrigerator and taste. It should be tart with a bit of sweetness and spice. Adjust flavors if necessary by adding more sugar or pepper. If it tastes watery, drain some liquid and add more vinegar.

Recipe Type	Calories	Total Fat (grams)	Carbs (grams)	Protein (grams)
Carb	86	0	21	2

Pad Thai with Almond Sauce

4 servings

  1 cup red cabbage, shredded (CT), or spinach, chopped (PT)

 ½ cup whole cilantro leaves

  1 teaspoon fresh lime juice

  2 tablespoons tamarind juice*

  2 tablespoons maple syrup

  2 tablespoons nama shoyu (raw soy sauce)*

  2 teaspoons minced garlic

  2 teaspoons minced fresh ginger

  1 teaspoon habanero chili, minced

  2 tablespoons olive oil

 ½ teaspoon sea salt

 ¼ cup yellow onion, sliced thinly

  1 cup cucumber, peeled and thinly sliced (CT), or green apple, cored and thinly sliced (PT)

 ½ cup red bell pepper, thinly sliced (CT), or green beans, thinly sliced (PT)

  1 Serrano pepper, thinly sliced

  3 cups coconut meat, thinly sliced

     Freshly ground pepper, to taste

     Sea Salt, to taste

  8 whole romaine lettuce leaves

     Almond Sauce (recipe follows)

continued on 237

Healthy Recipes for Your Nutritional Type

Almond Sauce:

- ½ cup raw almond butter
- 1½ tablespoons fresh ginger, grated
- 2 garlic cloves
- 1 red chili pepper
- 2 tablespoons fresh lemon juice
- 2 tablespoons maple syrup
- 1 tablespoon nama shoyu
- ¼ cup water, more if necessary

    Sea salt and freshly ground pepper, to taste

1. For the almond sauce: combine all ingredients in a blender and blend until smooth. Add more water if needed to thin. Set aside.

2. In a medium bowl combine the cabbage, cilantro, and lime juice. Sprinkle with salt and let sit for 30 minutes.

3. In a small bowl, whisk together tamarind juice, maple syrup, nama shoyu, garlic, ginger, chili, oil, and salt. Set aside.

4. Meanwhile combine the onion, cucumber, and bell pepper in a large bowl. Add the cabbage mixture and toss with the tamarind dressing.

5. On four serving plates arrange ¼ of the cabbage-vegetable mixture and top with the coconut. Drizzle the almond sauce on top.

Recipe Type	Calories	Total Fat (grams)	Carbs (grams)	Protein (grams)
Mixed	587	46	43	10
Carb	582	46	41	10
Protein	592	46	44	10

Pickled Vegetables with Arame

12 servings

> 1　cup rice vinegar
> 1　teaspoon olive oil
> ½　teaspoon kelp powder
> 2　bay leaves
> ¼　cup arame*, soaked
> 2　cups diced vegetables: celery, green beans, cauliflower, mushrooms, asparagus (PT), or red cabbage, green cabbage, cucumber, pearl onion, peppers (CT)

1. Combine rice vinegar, oil, kelp powder, and bay leaves in a small bowl. Set aside.

2. Rinse the arame, and then soak in cool water for 5–10 minutes. Drain and set aside.

3. Put diced vegetables into a pot of boiling water. Turn off the heat, cover, and let stand for 3–4 minutes. Drain.

4. Combine arame and vegetables in a sterilized jar. Pour marinade in, it should cover the vegetables.

5. Seal and refrigerate. It will keep in the refrigerator for several weeks.

*Arame is a sea vegetable and can usually be found in the Asian food aisle at the grocery store.

Recipe Type	Calories	Total Fat (grams)	Carbs (grams)	Protein (grams)
Mixed	31	1	7	1
Carb	27	1	5	2
Protein	36	1	8	1

Raw Sauerkraut

1 whole green cabbage
1 tablespoon grated fresh ginger
2 carrots, grated
1 tablespoon sea salt

1. Grate or slice thinly the cabbage and pound with mallet to release the juices. Save the outer leaves of the cabbage and set aside.

2. Shred the carrots and add to the cabbage. Mix in the ginger and salt.

3. Place in a ceramic pot or glass container.

4. Cover the mix with the saved outer leaves of the cabbage. Place a plate on top of the leaves. Put a 4 or 5 pound weight on the plate (a brick, a bottle of sand). Cover the container with a piece of cheesecloth and then with a loose lid.

5. Leave at room temperature for three days. Then refrigerate, it can be used after about a week or ten days.

6. When ready, remove the lid and the outer leaves and discard. Store the kraut in the refrigerator in a glass jar. It can be used immediately, however, it does improve with age.

Recipe Type	Calories	Total Fat (grams)	Carbs (grams)	Protein (grams)
Mixed	365	2	85	19

Raw Flax Crackers

6 servings

  1   cup golden flax seeds, soaked overnight

  1   medium onion, chopped

  1   jalapeno pepper, seeded and chopped (optional)

  1   cup spinach, chopped

  1   tablespoon nutritional yeast

  1   tablespoon tamari

  1   tablespoon dulse flakes*

  1   teaspoon garlic, chopped

1. After flax seeds have soaked overnight, drain them. They will remain sticky and wet. Place them in a food processor with chopping blade attachment.

2. Add the rest of the ingredients to the flax seeds. Blend in food processor.

3. Divide the mixture into four. Spread each fourth of the mixture onto a teflex sheet with an offset spatula and place in the food dehydrator set on 118°F. Do not go above 118°F as this will kill the valuable enzymes in the crackers.

4. Dehydrate for 8 hours then turn over and dehydrate for another 1–2 hours.

5. Remove the crackers from the dehydrator and gently remove from the teflex sheets. They will be very crispy, crunchy, and easily breakable, break each sheet into four or five pieces and keep in an airtight container until ready to use.

Continued on page 241

Note: These crackers can be served with guacamole, hummus or alone as a highly nutritious snack. They will keep for up to a month in an airtight container, but be aware they break very easily, so try not to move them around too much before serving them.

*Dulse is a sea vegetable that can be purchased at most health food stores.

Recipe Type	Calories	Total Fat (grams)	Carbs (grams)	Protein (grams)
Mixed	145	9	12	7

"Salmon" Wraps with Guacamole

6 servings

- 2 cups carrot pulp*
- 1 small avocado, cubed
- ½ cup fresh dill, chopped
- ¼ cup yellow onion, finely minced
- 2-3 tablespoons lemon juice
- 2 tablespoons ginger, finely minced
- 1 tablespoon garlic, finely minced
  Carrot juice, as needed for texture
- 1 cup raw sour cream (recipe follows) (PT)
- 1 cup guacamole (recipe follows)
- 6 large romaine lettuce leaves, without tears

1. Combine carrot pulp, avocado, dill, onion, lemon juice, ginger, and garlic in a large bowl. Mix well. Add carrot juice if the mixture is dry. Set aside while preparing the raw sour cream and guacamole.

2. Once all ingredients are ready, assemble the wraps. Place a lettuce leaf on a plate; spread the "salmon" mixture along the center. Add raw sour cream and guacamole as desired.

Raw Sour Cream: (PT)

- 1 cup raw macadamia nuts, soaked overnight
- 1 cup raw cashews, soaked overnight
- ½ cup fresh lemon juice
- 1½ teaspoons sea salt
- ¾ tablespoon garlic
- ¼ teaspoon black peppercorns
  Water, as needed for thinning

continued on 243

1. In a food processor add all ingredients, except water. Blend until mixture is creamy, adding water in small increments to achieve a sour cream like consistency.

Guacamole:

　　2　medium avocados, ripe

　　3　tablespoons lemon juice

　½　bunch cilantro, chopped

　¼　cup chopped red onion

　　1　teaspoon Serrano chili, seeds removed and finely minced

　　　Sea salt, to taste

1. Place avocados in a medium bowl and mash with a fork. Add remaining ingredients and mix well. Add salt to taste.

Recipe Type	Calories	Total Fat (grams)	Carbs (grams)	Protein (grams)
Mixed	227	16	22	5
Carb	609	50	38	14
Raw Sour Cream (Add-On)	382	34	16	9
Guacamole (Add-On)	127	10	9	3

Spicy Chopped Zucchini (CT)

4 servings

- 1 large zucchini, chopped
- 2 tablespoons chopped red onion
- 1 red bell pepper, chopped
- 1 jalapeno pepper, seeds removed and chopped
- ¼ cup chopped cilantro
- 1 clove garlic, minced
- 1   tablespoon tamari soy sauce
- 1 tablespoon lemon juice
- 1 cup bean sprouts
- 1 lemon, cut into 4 wedges

1. In a large mixing bowl, combine the zucchini, onion, bell pepper, jalapeno pepper, cilantro, and garlic. Add the tamari and lemon. Toss to combine. Adjust flavors if desired with additional tamari and lemon juice.

2. Place ¼ cup bean sprouts on each individual chilled plate. Garnish each with a lemon wedge.

Recipe Type	Calories	Total Fat (grams)	Carbs (grams)	Protein (grams)
Carb	28	0	6	2

Sunflower Scallion Dip

12 servings

  2 cups sunflower seeds, soaked 4 hours
  ½ cup water, or more for a lighter texture
  ⅓ cup lemon juice, up to ½ cup
  ½ cup tahini
  ¼ cup miso, light
 1½ teaspoons celtic sea salt
  1 tablespoon onion powder
  2 cloves garlic, up to 4 cloves
  ⅛ teaspoon cayenne
  ½ bunch parsley, chopped
  8 scallions, chopped

1. Puree everything except scallions and parsley until smooth and creamy, adding extra water if necessary.

2. Pulse in scallions and parsley at the end for a whiter color.

CT: Serve with raw broccoli spears, cucumbers and peppers.

PT: Add 1 cup raw plain yogurt and serve with cauliflower spears.

Recipe Type	Calories	Total Fat (grams)	Carbs (grams)	Protein (grams)
Mixed	220	18	11	7
Carb	230	19	13	7
Protein	237	18	14	8

Thai Coconut Soup

4 servings

1½ cups water
  2 cups coconut water (see note below)
  2 cups young coconut meat
  1 cup fresh cherry tomatoes
 ½ ripe avocado
  1 clove garlic
  1 inch fresh ginger
  2 tablespoons white miso
  1 tablespoon flax seed oil
 ½ teaspoon sea salt
  2 tablespoons nama shoyu* or wheat-free tamari soy sauce
  2 limes
 ⅛ teaspoon cayenne
  1 cup cilantro
 ⅓ cup shallots chopped
  1 stalk lemongrass, cut into 2 inch pieces
  1 carrot, sliced very thinly

1. Blend all ingredients in a high-speed blender except for last 4. Add the cilantro and blend briefly, so that you can still see small pieces of cilantro.

2. Pour into a bowl and stir in last 3 ingredients.

continued on 247

Healthy Recipes for Your Nutritional Type

Note: *You can find coconut water and coconut meat by breaking opening young green coconuts (sold in some conventional grocery stores and Asian markets.) If you cannot find these young coconuts, you can also use canned or bottled coconut water and canned coconut meat or 3 cups of canned coconut milk.*

*Nama shoyu is a blend of raw shoyu (soy sauce) and can be found at health food stores.

Recipe Type	Calories	Total Fat (grams)	Carbs (grams)	Protein (grams)
Mixed	298	20	29	7

Zucchini Alfredo

4 servings

    3 zucchinis

1½ cup macadamia nuts, soaked overnight

    2 tablespoons walnuts, soaked overnight

  ¼ cup olive oil

    2 teaspoons sea salt

    3 small cloves garlic

    2 teaspoons fresh ground pepper

      Water, for sauce consistency

1. Peel skin from the zucchinis using a vegetable peeler. Discard green skin. Use the vegetable peeler to make long, flat fettuccini-like noodles, until you reach the center part with seeds. Discard the remaining center and set aside "noodles."

2. In a blender combine the remaining ingredients and blend until smooth, adding water as necessary for desired consistency.

3. Pour sauce over bowl of zucchini and serve immediately.

PT: Serve with very thinly sliced raw beef—carpaccio style. (Freeze grass-fed beef tenderloin wrapped in plastic wrap for 2 hours. Unwrap and slice thinly, about 1/8-inch thick pieces. Cover with plastic wrap and pound with a meat mallet until paper-thin.)

Recipe Type	Calories	Total Fat (grams)	Carbs (grams)	Protein (grams)
Mixed	517	55	10	6
Protein	664	63	10	24

Snacks

Snacks

Snacks are no longer just for kids. In fact, they are a very important piece of the *Take Control Of Your Health Program*. Choosing healthy foods is as important at snack time as at mealtime. Snacks can add fiber and nutrients to your diet without unwanted calories. They can give you an energy boost during the day and prevent you from overeating at meals, and they can also stabilize your blood sugar. The trick to snacks is to plan ahead so that you do not get yourself into a situation where you are too hungry, and ready to grab anything to eat, good or bad.

Think of a snack as a "mini meal" that will help you have a healthy diet, rather than as an opportunity to consume treats. With proper portions and the correct food choices, snacking will enhance, not hinder, your diet. In addition to the snack recipes in this section, please also remember that any leftovers that remain from any of the other recipes you have prepared, would make excellent snack choices. In fact, it is recommended that you prepare more than you need for any given meal, in order to have extra portions of already prepared food on hand. This will not only save time preparing additional snacks, it will ensure that you have something healthy to grab between meals.

Of course planning your snacks is the key to success. It is not wise to wait until you are starving to look for a snack. In addition to leftovers, now that you know your individual metabolic type, you can be sure to have snack food on hand that is easily transportable, such as cut up organic vegetables, cubes of raw cheese, small containers of salad-ready lettuce and salad dressing, or hummus. In addition to the recipes shared in this book, below is a list of snack ideas:

- Fresh organic fruit or a handful of dried fruit
- Fresh raw organic vegetables—such as cut up carrots, celery, red and green pepper, with nut butter or yogurt.
- Whole grain or rice crackers with nut butter or cheese
- Yogurt and berries
- A handful of raw nuts and/or seeds
- Hummus and carrot sticks
- A homemade smoothie with yogurt, raw egg, fruit, and/or whey powder
- A piece of cold leftover chicken or turkey with raw veggie of choice
- Roast beef slices with Dijon mustard and cucumber
- Hard boiled eggs
- Romaine lettuce leaves with turkey and avocado

Chicken Liver Pate (PT)

8 servings

8	ounces chicken liver
1	cup sliced mushrooms
2	tablespoons butter
2	tablespoons olive oil
½	cup chopped yellow onions
1	clove garlic, minced
2	tablespoons cognac , or other dark alcohol
½	teaspoon of salt
⅛	teaspoon of freshly ground black pepper
⅛	teaspoon of cayenne pepper
¼	teaspoon of powdered allspice
	Milk, as needed for consistency

1. Wash, dry, and chop livers.

2. Sauté mushrooms in butter and olive oil for 5 minutes. Remove mushrooms with a slotted spoon and set aside.

3. In the same pan add onions, liver, and garlic and cook 5 minutes. Remove from heat and cool slightly.

4. Put all ingredients in a blender or food processor. Cover and blend until mixture is well combined. If mixture is too thick, add some milk (1 tablespoon at a time).

5. Pack in crocks or a mold and refrigerate for 4–24 hours. Serve in the crocks or unmold and serve on a small plate. Will taste best at room temperature.

Recipe Type	Calories	Total Fat (grams)	Carbs (grams)	Protein (grams)
Protein	116	9	2	8

Cinnamon Flax Fruit

4 servings

    1 teaspoon ground cinnamon
    4 tablespoons flax seeds
       Sliced banana or apple

1. Grind the flax seeds in a coffee grinder. Add cinnamon.

2. Top fruit with flax mix.

PT: Use bananas and green apples that are not fully ripe (and therefore contain less sugar).

Recipe Type	Calories	Total Fat (grams)	Carbs (grams)	Protein (grams)
Mixed	88	4	12	3
Protein	94	4	13	3

Crudités with Tangy Garlic-Scallion Dip

10 servings

- 1 red bell pepper (CT), or 8 ounces sliced mushrooms (PT)
- 1 yellow bell pepper (CT), or ½ head cauliflower, cut in florets (PT)
- 8 celery stalks
- 2 tablespoons diced scallions
- 2 tablespoons minced garlic
- 1 tablespoon fresh minced ginger
- 2 tablespoons tamari soy sauce
- 3 tablespoons almond butter
- 2 tablespoons brown rice syrup
- 1 15-ounce can chickpeas, drained
- 3 tablespoons rice wine vinegar
- ½ teaspoon Tabasco
- 2 tablespoons gomasio (ground sesame seeds and sea salt)
- ½ teaspoon sea salt

1. Cut peppers and celery into strips.

2. In a food processor, combine scallions, garlic, ginger, tamari, almond butter, rice syrup, chickpeas, vinegar, and hot sauce. Blend for about 4 minutes.

3. With the food processor running, add the gomasio and salt and blend for another 30 seconds.

4. Place dip in a bowl and place on a chilled platter. Spread the cut-up vegetables around dip bowl and serve.

Recipe Type	Calories	Total Fat (grams)	Carbs (grams)	Protein (grams)
Mixed	126	5	18	5
Carb	125	5	18	5
Protein	127	5	18	5

Cumin Spiced Lettuce Roll (MT)

4–5 servings

- 1 head leaf lettuce (butter or red leaf)
- 1 avocado, peeled and sliced into strips
- 2 scallions, minced
- 1 red pepper, minced
-    Alfalfa sprouts

Dressing:

- 3 tablespoons fresh lemon juice
- 1 teaspoon honey
- 1 teaspoon ground cumin
- ½ teaspoon cayenne pepper
-    Salt to taste
- ¼ cup olive oil

1. Cut out the lettuce cores. Separate leaves.

2. Top with some minced scallions and a few pieces of red pepper. Add some sprouts and roll the leaf carefully.

3. Secure with toothpick. Continue the process with the remaining ingredients.

4. Whisk together lemon juice through salt. Then add olive oil. Serve with lettuce rolls.

Recipe Type	Calories	Total Fat (grams)	Carbs (grams)	Protein (grams)
Mixed	198	17	11	3

Deviled Eggs

12 servings

- 6 eggs, hard boiled
- 1 ripe avocado, diced
- 1 tablespoon fresh lemon juice
- 2 tablespoons plain yogurt (PT), or low-fat plain yogurt (CT)
- ½ teaspoon Dijon mustard
  Sea salt and pepper, to taste
  Paprika, to garnish

1. Cut each egg in half lengthwise and remove yolks. Place yolks in a bowl and mash with a fork. Add the avocado and lemon juice and mash together with yolks.

2. Add the yogurt and mustard. Season to taste with salt and pepper.

3. Spoon yolk mixture evenly into egg white halves. Garnish with a sprinkling of paprika.

Recipe Type	Calories	Total Fat (grams)	Carbs (grams)	Protein (grams)
Mixed	72	5	3	4
Carb	73	5	3	4
Protein	73	5	3	4

Garlic Hummus with Celery and Pita Crisps

4–6 servings

  2 cups garbanzo beans
  ¼ cup tahini
      Juice of 3 lemons
  2 garlic cloves
      Salt, to taste
  2 celery stalks, sliced
      Pita crisps (recipe follows)

1. In a food processor or blender combine all ingredients and blend until smooth. Serve with celery slices and pita crisps.

Pita Crisps:

  2 whole wheat pita breads
  ⅛ cup olive oil
      Coarse salt, to taste
      Freshly ground pepper, to taste

1. Preheat oven to 350°F. Split the pita breads in half horizontally, brush cut sides with olive oil. Cut each round into eight wedges.

2. Arrange, cut sides up, on a rimmed baking sheet. Sprinkle with coarse salt and ground pepper. Bake until golden and crisp, 10 to 12 minutes.

Note: For a low-carb, wheat-free substitution, you may also use the hummus as a vegetable dip instead of using pita crisps.

Recipe Type	Calories	Total Fat (grams)	Carbs (grams)	Protein (grams)
Mixed	372	11	56	16

Grilled Skewers of Apples
and Spinach-Chicken Sausage (PT)

4 servings

4 spinach-chicken sausages, each cut into 4 pieces

2 large green apples, each cut into 8 pieces

1 medium onion

lime wedges, for serving

1. Cut the onion in eighths: First, cut it from the top to root into quarters; then cut each quarter in half crosswise. This makes it easy to separate the onion into individual layers.

2. Thread the sausage pieces on skewers, alternating them with pieces of apple and onion.

3. Heat the grill to high. Place the sausage skewers on the grill until the sausage browns.

4. Remove and serve with lime wedges.

Recipe Type	Calories	Total Fat (grams)	Carbs (grams)	Protein (grams)
Protein	248	12	24	12

Pan Toasted Cayenne Almonds and Pumpkin Seeds (PT)

4 servings

- ½ cup raw almonds
- ½ cup raw pumpkin seeds
-    cayenne pepper, to taste

1. Heat a small cast iron skillet over medium heat. Add almonds and pumpkin seeds with a sprinkle of cayenne pepper, to taste. Stirring frequently, toast until nuts and seeds are lightly browned. Remove from pan immediately.

2. Divide into four portions and serve.

Recipe Type	Calories	Total Fat (grams)	Carbs (grams)	Protein (grams)
Mixed	140	11	8	5

Spinach-Parmesan Stuffed Mushrooms

6 servings

- 12 large mushrooms
- 2 tablespoons minced shallots
- 1 clove garlic, minced
- 2 tablespoons olive oil
- 1 cup finely chopped fresh spinach (PT), or chard (CT)
- ¼ cup pine nuts, chopped fine
- ¼ cup grated parmesan cheese
- 2 tablespoons flat leaf parsley, chopped fine

1. Preheat oven to 425°F.

2. Wipe the mushrooms clean and gently remove the stems. Set caps aside.

3. Chop the mushroom stems to make 1 cup.

4. Heat the olive oil in a medium sauté pan over medium high heat until glistening. Add the mushroom stems, shallots, and garlic; sauté until tender and just starting to brown. Stir in the spinach, pine nuts, cheese, and parsley. Cook until spinach wilts, about 1–2 minutes.

5. Spoon spinach mixture into mushroom caps. Place stuffed mushrooms on a lightly oiled baking dish and cook for 8–10 minutes.

Recipe Type	Calories	Total Fat (grams)	Carbs (grams)	Protein (grams)
Mixed	113	10	4	4
Carb	115	10	4	5
Protein	110	10	3	4

Sprout Stuffed Tomatoes (MT)

4 servings

- 4 ripe avocados
- 3 large ripe tomatoes, chopped
- 1 packed cup alfalfa or sunflower sprouts, coarsely chopped
  Juice of 2 lemons
- 1 garlic clove, pressed
- 2 scallions, minced
- 2 teaspoons fresh cilantro, minced
  Drizzle umeboshi vinegar
  Toasted sesame seeds

1. Slice avocados lengthwise, remove pit, and set aside 4 halves. Mix remaining ingredients.

2. Smash remaining avocados, and mix with tomatoes, sprouts, lemon juice, garlic, scallions, and cilantro.

3. Stuff the 4 avocado halves with the tomato mixture.

4. Sprinkle with umeboshi vinegar and toasted sesame seeds

Recipe Type	Calories	Total Fat (grams)	Carbs (grams)	Protein (grams)
Mixed	404	32	32	9

Sunflower Loaf

12 servings

1   tablespoon coconut oil

1   medium red onion, chopped

1   cup cooked brown rice

3   cloves garlic, minced

1   cup sunflower seeds, raw, soaked overnight

¼   cup warm water

⅓   cup melted raw butter or olive oil

½   cup flour

½   cup nutritional yeast

¼   cup tamari

1½ teaspoons dried basil

1   tablespoon toasted sesame seeds

1. Preheat oven to 350°F. Brush oil onto 2 loaf pans.

2. Place all the ingredients in a food processor or blender and blend until smooth.

3. Pour the mixture into pans. Bake 40 minutes, or till firm.

4. Loosen loaves from pans with a spatula and empty onto a cooling rack. Once cooled, wrap well in plastic to store.

5. Can be stored in refrigerator for up to 2 weeks.

CT: Eat this sparingly as seeds are not your ideal food.

Recipe Type	Calories	Total Fat (grams)	Carbs (grams)	Protein (grams)
Mixed	192	14	14	6

Summertime Avocado Bruschetta

6 servings

2 avocados, cut into ½-inch pieces

2 scallions, chopped

2 small tomatoes, seeded and diced

2 tablespoons fresh lime juice

1 tablespoon white wine vinegar

1 tablespoon extra virgin olive oil

2 teaspoons hot sauce

½ teaspoon garlic powder

½ teaspoon salt

¼ cup chopped fresh cilantro

Baguette:*

3 tablespoons olive oil

1 clove of garlic, finely minced

½ teaspoon salt

36 whole-wheat French bread slices

1. Combine all ingredients, except cilantro, in a bowl; toss gently to combine. Cover and chill for 2 hours.

2. Preheat oven at 375°F. Combine the 3 tablespoons of olive oil, garlic, and salt. Spread bread slices in a single-layer on a baking pan, and brush evenly with the olive oil and garlic mixture. Bake for 10 minutes or until toasted; cool.

3. Top each toast evenly with avocado mixture. Sprinkle with cilantro before serving.

Continued on page 263

For a wheat-free alternative, serve on wheat-free bread, crispy rice or flax crackers, or as a filling in a romaine lettuce leaf.

PT: Instead of serving avocado mixture on bread or crackers, serve over a piece of grilled chicken thigh, or add 1 cup of cooked and diced chicken thigh to avocado mixture and serve in a romaine lettuce leaf.

Recipe Type	Calories	Total Fat (grams)	Carbs (grams)	Protein (grams)
Mixed	330	26	10	20
Protein	290	22	8	17

Avocado Mixture:

Calories	Total Fat (grams)	Carbs (grams)	Protein (grams)
120	11	7	2

Avocado + Chicken Thigh Without Skin:

Calories	Total Fat (grams)	Carbs (grams)	Protein (grams)
202	14	7	15.5

Avocado + With Skin:

Calories	Total Fat (grams)	Carbs (grams)	Protein (grams)
318	25	7	18

Carb Type (Avocado + Baguette):

Calories	Total Fat (grams)	Carbs (grams)	Protein (grams)
440	32	43	4

Baguette calories are so high due to 6 pieces baguette per serving.

Super Boost Power Smoothie

4 servings

- 4 cups rice milk (CT), or almond milk (PT)
- 1 large banana
- 2 tablespoons Whey protein powder or 4 raw eggs
- 1 tablespoon bee pollen
- ¼ cup almond butter (PT)
- 1 teaspoon spirulina or other green powder
- 2 tablespoons flax seeds
- 1 cup blueberries
- 1 inch piece fresh ginger
- 2 teaspoons lemon juice
- 2 fluid ounces aloe vera juice
- 2 cups water

1. Place all ingredients into a blender. Mix until smooth.

Recipe Type	Calories	Total Fat (grams)	Carbs (grams)	Protein (grams)
Mixed	425	25	36	19
Carb	425	25	37	18
Protein	426	25	36	19

Yogurt-Spinach Dip

4 servings

- 2 cups steamed spinach
- 1 tablespoon olive oil
- 1 cup chopped green onions
- 1 tablespoon minced garlic
- 1 cup plain yogurt (PT), or low-fat yogurt (CT)
- ½ cup finely grated raw parmesan cheese
- 2 tablespoons fresh lemon juice
- ⅛ teaspoon cayenne pepper
- Sea salt and freshly ground pepper

1. Place cooked spinach in a colander; squeeze out all excess liquid.

2. In a medium skillet over medium heat, heat oil until shimmering. Add the onions and garlic. Cook, stirring often until fragrant and softened, about 2 minutes.

3. Transfer into a bowl. Add the spinach, yogurt, cheese, lemon juice, cayenne pepper and salt, to taste. Mix well and put in serving bowl.

PT: Serve with celery sticks and cauliflower florets.

CT: Serve with bell pepper strips and broccoli florets.

Recipe Type	Calories	Total Fat (grams)	Carbs (grams)	Protein (grams)
Mixed	150	9	10	9
Carb	151	8	11	10
Protein	149	9	9	9

Desserts

Chocolate Cake

8 servings

- 1½ cups spelt flour
- ½ teaspoon xanthan gum*
- ½ cup unsweetened cocoa powder
- ¼ teaspoon baking powder
- ½ teaspoon baking soda
- ¼ teaspoon salt
- ⅔ cup ground almonds (soaked overnight, dehydrated)
- ¾ cup butter
- 1 cup sugar
- 2 eggs, beaten
- 1½ teaspoons vanilla extract
- 1 cup chocolate milk

1. Preheat oven to 350°F

2. Prepare two 8-inch round cake pans and grease.

3. Sift flour, xanthan gum, cocoa, baking powder, baking soda, and salt in medium bowl.

4. Mix in the ground nuts. Set aside.

5. Using a food processor blend the butter and add the sugar. Add eggs and vanilla. Then add the milk and flour mixture. Blend well, but not too much.

6. Pour batter into prepared cake pans and bake for 25–30 minutes. Test for doneness with a toothpick; if it comes out clean it's done.

7. Let stand for 10 minutes before turning out onto wire rack. Can be frosted or served plain.

* *Can be purchased at health food store.*

Recipe Type	Calories	Total Fat (grams)	Carbs (grams)	Protein (grams)
Mixed	440	26	51	7

Banana Ice Cream

Makes 1 quart

- 4 over-ripe bananas
- 2 tablespoons lecithin granules (optional, but adds creamy texture)
- 1½ cups milk (or coconut milk, or nut/rice milk, or half and half)
- ¼ cup sugar
- 1 teaspoon vanilla

1. In a food processor liquefy the bananas and the lecithin granules. While processor is still running add the remaining ingredients. Or, in an Omega juicer homogenize the bananas and mix with the remaining ingredients.

2. Depending on the size of the bananas, this will make up to 4 cups liquid. Add more milk if necessary to make one-quart of liquid. Pour the mixture into baking sheets or ice-cube trays and freeze until solid.

3. If using baking sheets, cut the frozen mixture into strips, if using ice-cube trays just pop out the cubes. Place frozen pieces back into juicer or food processor and blend until homogenized. Serve immediately.

Note: Ice cream will be thicker and creamier if the juicer body, cutter, blank, and bowl are chilled in the refrigerator 30 minutes before using.

Continued on page 271

Variations:

Chocolate-Banana:

Add ½ cup cocoa or carob powder and an additional teaspoon of vanilla to the above recipe.

Tropical: (CT)

Use 2 over-ripe bananas, ½ cup strawberries, ½ cup finely cut pineapple, 1½ cups milk, 2 tablespoons lecithin granules (optional), and ½ cup sugar.

Coconut: (PT)

Use 2 eggs, 3 tablespoons lecithin granules, 3 cups coconut milk, ⅓ cup sugar, and 1 teaspoon vanilla.

Recipe Type	Calories	Total Fat (grams)	Carbs (grams)	Protein (grams)
Mixed	261	10	44	4
Carb	286	11	47	4
Protein	286	11	50	4

Flourless Honey Almond Cookies

Makes one dozen cookies

- 2 large egg whites
- 1 pinch cream of tartar
- 2 tablespoons honey
- ½ teaspoon vanilla
- 1 pinch salt
- 1 cup almonds, ground

1. Preheat oven to 250°F. If not using a nonstick sheet, then lightly butter a regular cookie sheet.

2. Beat egg whites and the cream of tartar until stiff peaks form, and then gradually beat in honey, vanilla, and lemon zest.

3. Gently fold in ground almonds.

4. Drop 1 tablespoon of batter at a time onto prepared baking sheet, spacing about 2 inches apart. Bake for about 30 minutes. These cookies are soft right out of the oven but harden as they cool.

PT: Option to add 1 cup chopped walnuts.

CT: Serve with fresh berries or peach slices.

Recipe Type	Calories	Total Fat (grams)	Carbs (grams)	Protein (grams)
Mixed	60	4	5	2
Carb	65	4	6	2
Protein	124	10	8	4

Lemon Coconut Pudding

6 servings

- 2 cups coconut, young
- ½ teaspoon lemon extract
- 1 teaspoon vanilla
- ½ teaspoon almond extract
- 1½ tablespoons lemon juice
- 2 drops stevia
- ½ teaspoon honey, to balance
- 1 pinch sea salt
- 1 cup water, in increments
- 1 cup ice cubes

1. In a high-speed blender, blend all ingredients, except ice, until smooth. Taste and adjust sweet balance. Add the ice and blend again until cool and creamy. Serve in small ramekin dishes.

2. Garnish with lemon zest.

Recipe Type	Calories	Total Fat (grams)	Carbs (grams)	Protein (grams)
Mixed	121	10	9	1

Yam "Chips" with Cinnamon and Nutmeg

4 servings

- 2 **large yams, sliced ¼-inch thick**
  Olive oil, to drizzle
- 1 **tablespoon ground cinnamon**
- 1 **teaspoon grated nutmeg**
  Honey, to drizzle

1. Preheat oven to 450°F.

2. Place sliced yams in a rectangular glass dish. Drizzle lightly with olive oil. Sprinkle with cinnamon and nutmeg. Drizzle with honey. Place in oven for 20 minutes.

3. Allow to cool slightly before serving.

Recipe Type	Calories	Total Fat (grams)	Carbs (grams)	Protein (grams)
Mixed	161	1	38	3

Yogurt with Vanilla, Cinnamon, Nutmeg, and Flax Seeds

4 servings

- 4 cups plain yogurt (PT), or low-fat plain yogurt (CT)
- 1½ tablespoons vanilla extract
- 1½ tablespoons cinnamon
- 2 teaspoons nutmeg
- 1 tablespoon maple syrup
- 2 tablespoons ground flax seeds (PT), or 1 tablespoon flax seeds (CT)

1. Mix all ingredients in a medium mixing bowl. Divide into 4 serving bowls. Serve immediately.

CT: Add fresh berries.

Recipe Type	Calories	Total Fat (grams)	Carbs (grams)	Protein (grams)
Mixed	215	8	27	12
Carb	239	6	35	14
Protein	206	11	20	10

Information About Unusual Recipe Ingredients

Arrowroot

A grain free thickener made from the root of the tropical arrowroot plant. Unlike flour, once thickened, it is clear.

Celeriac or Celery Root

The root of a celery raised specifically for its root. It looks similar to a brown turnip, but is knobby. The flavor is like strong celery mixed with parsley. Choose a firm smaller sized root with a minimum of knobs.

Crème Fraiche

Similar to sour cream, but thicker. An advantage to using crème fraiche is that it can be boiled without curdling.

Daikon

Japanese radish. A white root similar in shape to a carrot. Choose daikon that is firm and unwrinkled.

Fish Sauce

A condiment and seasoning liquid made from salted, fermented fish. Can come in various flavors. A wide variety can be found in Asian markets.

Garam Masala

Blend of ground spices originating from India. May contain up to 12 spices but exact mixtures depend on the taste of the preparer. It can include the following spices: bay leaves, black pepper, cinnamon, cloves, coriander, cumin, cardamom, dried chilies, fennel, mace, nutmeg, turmeric, along with other spices. May be purchased in most supermarkets or made at home.

Ghee

Butter that has been slowly cooked until the milk solids separate from the liquid. Ghee is a form of clarified butter that cooks until all the liquid evaporates and the solids begin to brown. The result is a nutty flavor and a butter that can be cooked at higher temperatures. May be purchased in most supermarkets or made at home.

Gomasio

A seasoning made from toasted sesame seeds and sea salt. Can be purchased in most health food stores or Asian markets, or made at home.

Kaffir Lime Leaves

The leaf of a plant grown in Southeast Asia that is a seasoning ingredient often used in Thai soups, stir-fries, and curries.

Kudzu

A thickener made from the root of the kudzu vine, often used instead of flour, cornstarch or arrowroot because of its superior essence and because it continues to thicken while cooling. Can be found in most Asian markets and some natural food stores.

Lemon Grass

An herb that imparts a sour-lemon flavor and fragrance often used in Thai cooking. Available in Asian markets and some supermarkets.

Mirin

Also referred to as rice wine or sake, mirin adds mild sweetness to a variety of sauces, vinaigrettes, vegetable dishes, and fish dishes.

Miso

Fermented soybean paste that is used as a flavoring in many Japanese dishes. It is also used as a seasoning agent in place of Worcestershire sauce, salt or soy sauce. It should be added at the end of cooking, as heat will destroy miso's beneficial microorganisms.

Nama Shoyu

Raw, organic, unpasteurized soy sauce often used the raw food cuisine.

Nutritional Yeast

An exceptionally nutrient dense food that has a slightly sweet and nutty taste. It has a rich protein content with a high vitamin B profile. It can be sprinkled on a variety of foods as desired.

Spirulina

A microalgae which can be found in powdered form or in capsules or tablets. A highly nutritious food often mixed into smoothies or other drinks.

Stevia

A natural sweetener made from an herb that is sweeter than sugar but essentially non-caloric and cannot be metabolized in the human digestive system. Can be found in most natural food stores.

Tahini

A thick paste made from ground sesame seeds. Can be found in most supermarkets and natural food stores.

Tamari

Similar to soy sauce but thicker. It is available in wheat and wheat-free varieties. Often considered superior to everyday soy sauce because soy often contains preservatives and is chemically processed.

Tamarind

A seasoning agent that comes from the fruit of a tamarind tree. A popular flavoring in East Indian and Middle Eastern cuisines. Usually used in paste form and can be found in Indian and Asian markets.

Tempeh

A fermented food made from soybeans. It has a hearty texture with a yeasty, nutty flavor. It is high in protein and low in fat. It is often used as a meat substitute because of its heartiness, ability to absorb flavors, and ability to hold its shape when cooked.

Turmeric

A seasoning agent that comes from the root of a plant related to ginger. It lends a yellow-orange color to foods as well as a warm, musky aroma. It is an essential ingredient of curry dishes.

Umeboshi—paste or vinegar

A Japanese seasoning agent made from pickled Japanese plums. It tastes very salty and tart, making it a good replacement for salt and vinegar in many recipes. It can be found in Asian markets and natural food stores.

Xanthan gum

Used as a thickener and emulsifier in foods. It is made from the fermentation of corn sugar.

Juicing For Your Nutritional Type

Juicing is an amazing way to accelerate your physical journey to optimal health. However, it is important to understand your nutritional type prior to starting a juicing program. Please refer to my book *Take Control of Your Health* for more complete information about Nutritional Typing.

According to Nutritional Typing principles, if you are a carb type, vegetable juicing is strongly recommended. With the patients in our clinic, we strongly encourage it if they expect to regain their health. If you are a mixed type, it is certainly useful to juice. However, protein types need to follow some specific guidelines to make it work for them.

Protein Types and Juicing

If you are a protein type, juicing needs to be done cautiously. The only vegetables that should be juiced are your prime protein type vegetables, which are celery, spinach, asparagus, string beans, and cauliflower (including the base).

It is important to keep your serving size of juice to no more than 6 oz., but don't be surprised if you find that as little as 3–4 oz. of juice feels like the right serving size for you. For a protein type, 3–4 oz. of juice is a significant amount.

Also, to make drinking vegetable juice compatible with protein type metabolism (which needs high amounts of fat), it's important to blend a source of raw fat into the juice. Raw cream, raw butter, raw eggs, avocado, coconut butter, or freshly ground flax seed meal are the sources of raw fat that we most recommend. In addition to adding a source of raw fat to your juice, you may also find that adding some or even all of the vegetable pulp into your juice helps to make drinking the juiced vegetables more satisfying to you.

Beating Hepatitis C and Arthritis

I came to see Dr. Mercola for hepatitis C and arthritis. The biggest change that I made was in following the Take Control of Your Health program and eating for my nutritional type. Within a

Continued on page 282

week of making the changes, I noticed a difference in how I felt. I began vegetable juicing and I now drink the juice with every meal. I eat as much organic food as possible along with virtually no sugar or grain. My cravings for sugar and my old way of eating are gone. A great side effect of the program is that I've lost over 35 pounds in two months… and my arthritis has improved. Since starting the program, I can honestly say I've never felt better.

—Brian McIntyre

Some Reasons to Juice

Here are three main reasons why you will want to consider incorporating vegetable juicing into your health program:

1. Juicing helps you absorb all the nutrients from the vegetables.

This is important because most of us have impaired digestion as a result of making less-than-optimal food choices over many years. This limits your body's ability to absorb all the nutrients from the vegetables. Juicing will help to "pre-digest" them for you, so you will receive most of the nutrition, rather than having it go down the toilet.

2. Juicing allows you to consume an optimal amount of vegetables in an efficient manner.

If you are a carb type, you should eat one pound of raw vegetables per 50 pounds of body weight per day. Some people may find eating that many vegetables difficult, but you can easily accomplish it with a quick glass of vegetable juice.

3. You can add a wider variety of vegetables in your diet.

Many people eat the same vegetable salads everyday. This violates the principle of regular food rotation and increases your chance of developing an allergy to a certain food. But with juicing, you can experience a wide variety of vegetables that you may not normally eat.

If you are new to juicing, I recommend a mid-priced juicer. The cheap centrifugal juicers (like the Juiceman) break easily, produce low quality juice and are very loud, which may contribute to hearing loss.

My favorite juicer is the Omega Juicer. (See Appendix B)

Many of my patients thought that juicing would be a real chore, but the majority were pleasantly surprised to find that it was much easier than they thought it would be. This is partly related to the fact that you should only start by juicing vegetables that you enjoy eating non-juiced. The juice should taste pleasant—not make you nauseous.

It is important to listen to your body when juicing. Your stomach should be happy all morning long. If it is churning, growling, or generally making its presence known, you probably juiced something you should not be eating. Personally, I've noticed that I can't digest large amounts of cabbage, but if I spread it out over time, I do fine.

Lesson 1: Drink vegetable juice for breakfast.

Vegetable juice is a great breakfast when balanced with some essential oils and a bit of chlorella. Please remember that vegetable juice and fruit juices are two completely different substances in terms of nutrition. Ideally, you should avoid fruit juices. Although vegetable juice is processed, it doesn't raise insulin levels like fruit juice. The only exceptions would be carrot and beet juice (and most vegetables that grow underground), which function similarly to fruit juice.

Lesson 2: Get ready to juice!

Step 1: Now that you're ready for the benefits of vegetable juice, you need to know what to juice. I recommend starting out with these vegetables, as they are the easiest to digest:

- Celery

- Fennel (anise)

- Cucumbers

These aren't as nutrient dense as the dark green vegetables, which should be avoided if you are a protein type (with exception of spinach). Once you get used to these initial three vegetables, you can start adding the more nutritionally valuable, but less palatable, vegetables into your juice.

Vegetables to avoid include carrots and beets. Most people who juice usually use carrots. The reason they taste so good is that they are full of sugar. I would definitely avoid all vegetables that grow underground to avoid an increase in your insulin levels.

If you are healthy, you can add about one pound of carrots or beets per week. I do believe that the deep, intense colors of these foods provide additional benefits for many that are just not available in the green vegetables listed above.

Step 2: When you've acclimatized yourself to juicing, you can start adding these vegetables:

- Red leaf lettuce

- Green Leaf lettuce

- Romaine lettuce

- Endive

- Escarole

- Spinach

Step 3: After you're used to these, go to the next step:

- Cabbage

- Chinese Cabbage

- Bok Choy

Step 4: When you're ready, move on to adding herbs to your juicing. Herbs also make wonderful combinations. Here are two that work exceptionally well:

- Parsley

- Cilantro

You need to be cautious with cilantro, as many cannot tolerate it well. If you are new to juicing, hold off. These are more challenging vegetables to consume, but they are highly beneficial.

Step 5: The last step is to use just one or two of these leaves, as they are bitter:

- Kale

- Collard Greens

- Dandelion Greens

- Mustard Greens (bitter)

An interesting side note: cabbage juice is one of the most healing nutrients for ulcer repair, as it is a huge source of vitamin U.

When purchasing collard greens, find a store that sells the leaves still attached to the main stalk. If they have been cut off, the vegetable rapidly loses many of its valuable nutrients.

Lesson 3: Make your juice a balanced meal.

Balance your juice with protein and fat. Vegetable juice does not have much protein or fat, so it's very important for you to include these fat and protein sources with your meal.

- **Use eggs.** Eggs will add a significant amount of beneficial fats and protein to your meal. An egg has about 8 grams of protein, so you can add two to four eggs per meal. I suggest that you blend the whole eggs raw, right into the vegetable juice. The reason I advocate this is because once you heat the eggs, many of their nutrients become damaged. If you are concerned about salmonella, purchase organic eggs; it's unlikely you'll have any problems.

There is a potential problem with using the entire raw egg if you are pregnant. Biotin deficiency, a common concern in pregnancy, could be worsened by consuming whole, raw eggs.

- **For increased satiety, blend in some seeds.** If you get hungry easily after juicing, put your juice and seeds in the blender to make a higher fat drink. Seeds are full of protein and essential fatty acids that bring a juice into balance beautifully. I recommend pumpkin and flax seeds. If you use flax seeds, use a coffee grinder to grind them first and drink immediately after blending into the juice.

- **Use chlorella.** Chlorella is an incredibly powerful nutrient from the sea and is a form of algae. I use it quite a bit for mercury detoxification, as it binds strongly to mercury to eliminate it from the body. The normal dose is one teaspoon in the juice. However, about 30 percent of people cannot tolerate the chlorella. If it makes you nauseous, you should definitely avoid it. The advantages of chlorella are:

  - Provides a high source of chlorophyll

  - Adds magnesium and protein

  - Binds to heavy metals and pesticides to promote their removal from the body

If you have high iron or vitamin D levels, you will want to avoid chlorella, as it is loaded with both of these nutrients.

- **Add spirulina.** Spirulina is another algae that has many similar benefits and is a good balance to chlorella. However, it does not bind to heavy metals the way chlorella does.

- **Consider a protein powder.** I personally prefer to drink raw eggs for my breakfast protein. Fresh juice mixed with a protein powder is also a very convenient meal. Whey protein is the best type of powder as it is the most complete protein and the easiest to digest. Although whey protein is from milk and many people have lactose intolerance or an allergy to dairy, the major protein in milk that causes an allergy is casein.

Fortunately, whey protein does not contain casein. So, most people digest whey protein quite well. The most popular protein powders are the made from soy protein, which I do not recommend due to negative effects unfermented soy has on the body.

- **Add some garlic.** I like to add one clove of garlic in my juice, as it incorporates the incredible healing potential of fresh garlic. I strongly advise you to do this regularly to balance out your bowel flora. The ideal dose is just below the social threshold where people start to notice that you have eaten garlic. One large clove, two medium cloves, or three small cloves is the recommended dose.

- **Add oil.** But not just any oil! I highly recommend cod liver oil for the winter months and fish oil for the summer months.

However, if you live in a primarily sunny climate, I wouldn't advise taking cod liver oil. The reason for this is that cod liver oil has a level of vitamin D that can be toxic to those in very sunny climates. The dose for cod liver oil or fish oil is one teaspoon for every 25 to 40 pounds of body weight. Please note that cod liver oil can raise your vitamin D levels to unhealthy ranges. Ideally, you should have your doctor monitor your vitamin D levels with a blood test while taking cod liver oil.

The reason why adding oil (fat) to your vegetable juice may be helpful is that fat can help you better absorb the vitamin K from your vegetable juice (since vitamin K is a fat soluble vitamin). Vitamin K is very important for gluing the calcium into your bone matrix and helping you build stronger bones. Additionally, new research suggests that vitamin K significantly reduces calcification in the arteries.

Adding raw egg yolks, as described above, will also help you to absorb all the vitamin K from the juice. You could also use flax as a source of omega-3 fat, but many people have problems digesting it.

Lesson 4: Make your juice taste great.

If you would like to make your juice more palatable, especially in the beginning, you can add these elements:

- **Coconut:** This is one of my favorites! You can purchase the whole coconut or use unsweetened shredded coconut. It adds a delightful flavor and is an excellent source of fat to balance the meal. Coconut has medium chain triglycerides, which have many health benefits.

- **Cranberries:** You can also add some cranberries if you enjoy them. Researchers have discovered that cranberries have five times the antioxidant content of broccoli, which means they may protect against cancer, stroke, and heart disease. In addition, they are full of phytonutrients and can help women avoid urinary tract infections. Limit the cranberries to about 4 ounces per pint of juice.

- **Lemons:** You can also add half a lemon (leaving much of the white rind on). If you are a protein nutritional type, you will not want to use lemons, as they will push your pH in the wrong direction.

- **Fresh ginger:** This is an excellent addition if you can tolerate it. It gives your juice a little "kick".

Lesson 5: Drink your vegetable juice right away or store it very carefully.

Juicing is a time-consuming process, so you'll probably be thinking to yourself, "I wonder if I can juice first thing and then drink it later?" This isn't a great idea. Vegetable juice is perishable, so it's best to drink all of your juice immediately.

However, if you're careful, you can store your juice for up to 24 hours with only moderate nutritional decline.

To store your juice:

1. Put the juice in a glass jar with an airtight lid and fill it to the very top. There should be a minimum amount of air in the jar, as the oxygen in air (air is about 20 percent oxygen) will "oxidize" and damage the juice. You can also use a "Food Saver" (See TakeControlofYourHealth.com) if the juice is stored in a Ball jar, to evacuate the air from the container. This is not necessary if the jar is completely filled with fluid, but recommended if it is partially filled.

2. Wrap the jar with aluminum foil to block out all light. Light damages the juice.

3. Store it in the refrigerator until about 30 minutes prior to drinking, as vegetable juice should be consumed at room temperature.

Most people juice in the morning, but if that does not work out well for your schedule, please feel free to choose whatever mealtime works out best for your lifestyle.

Lesson 6: Clean your juicer properly.

We all know that if a juicer takes longer than 10 minutes to clean, we'll find excuses not to juice at all. I find that using an old toothbrush works well to clean any metal grater. For the Omega, the whole process takes about 5 minutes.

Whatever you do, you need to clean your juicer immediately after you juice to prevent any remnants from contaminating the juicer with mold growth.

WARNING: Don't follow the juicing recommendations that come with the juicer, as they most often emphasize the high sugar carrot and fruit combinations.

Juicing Helped Elizabeth Conquer Osteoporosis at 60

Here's a story from Elizabeth, one of our Optimal Wellness Center patients:

"As a woman approaching 60 years of age, I knew I didn't want to go the usual route of taking medicines for my recently diagnosed osteoporosis. Because I knew from past experience that taking potent drugs often left me feeling worse instead of better, I decided to take a more nontraditional approach to my healthcare and seek out the services of a holistic doctor.

I launched a search for holistic practitioners via the internet, and it was there that I found Dr. Mercola's Optimal Wellness Center and the wealth of information contained in his website, mercola.com.

On mercola.com, I read helpful article after helpful article until I was convinced that Dr. Mercola had the information and resources I needed to fight the debilitating disease that I knew osteoporosis could become.

I became a patient of the Optimal Wellness Center, and after receiving a thorough examination and evaluation, using several diagnostic tests and procedures, Dr. Mercola and his staff were able to determine a course of action that would put me on the road to better health.

Following their recommendations, I was gradually able to eliminate grains from my diet, drink plenty of fresh green vegetable

Continued on page 290

juices daily and eat those foods that an administered nutritional type test indicated would most benefit my health.

With my copy of "Dr. Mercola's *Take Control of Your Health Program*," in hand, I was well on my way to discovering delicious grain-free recipes (and I even invented a few of my own) to help me eat right for my nutritional type.

I was able to incorporate many other recommendations and lifestyle changes into my daily living. These included, among other things, drinking plenty of good quality water daily, weight training at the local fitness center, practicing methods of relaxation, and utilizing a technique called EFT (Emotional Freedom Technique) for the relief of physical as well as emotional pain.

After two years, I returned to my local hospital to repeat the bone density scan that had revealed my osteoporosis just two years prior. I was elated to find that not only had I stopped losing bone mass, but there was evidence that my bone mass had actually increased.

I was so relieved to know that my efforts had paid off and that by taking charge of my own health, I had found Dr. Mercola. I was glad, also, that I had made the necessary changes to my lifestyle that put me on the road to better health."

Recommended Ingredients and Products Locator

Most of the foods used in *Healthy Recipes For Your Nutritional Type* can be found in health food stores or grocery stores. If you can't find them there, or if you want further insight on the best forms and brands of these foods and products, you can consult these lists below.

The first list contains all the foods and other health products and services that I have researched extensively, that are typically more difficult to find in stores, and that I offer through the "Most Popular Products" section of Mercola.com.

The second list contains some specific foods and kitchen equipment that you can order direct from the suppliers or other online stores.

"Most Popular Products" on Mercola.com

Krill Oil

Krill Oil has more health-promoting antioxidants and omega-3 oils than fish oil. As a matter of fact, it has over 47 times the antioxidant value of fish oil, which helps prevent the perishable omega-3 from becoming rancid. Not only that, there's also no unpleasant aftertaste.

Coconut Oil, Virgin and Organic

Virgin coconut oil is highly recommended for your cooking, and has a wide range of proven health benefits. But quality can vary widely among brands, so you have to know what you are looking for. Fresh Shores and Garden of Life brand coconut oils meet all the necessary requirements, including certified organic, non-GMO, no "copra" or dried coconuts used, and no hydrogenation.

Cookware—5 Piece Enameled Cast Iron

Don't endanger your family's health with potentially toxic pots and pans, including Teflon, aluminum, stainless steel, and copper.

Now you can cook healthy and delicious meals at home with this gorgeous updated cast iron cookware. This set includes a 5-quart oval casserole with lid, 2-quart saucepan with lid, and 10-inch fry pan. This beautiful and affordable set comes with a limited lifetime warranty.

Coconut Flour

Replace the flour in your desserts with coconut flour and eat them guilt-free!

Coconut flour is free of gluten and low in digestible carbohydrates. It promotes a healthy heart and immune system. Plus, coconut flour is packed with fiber, so you'll feel full faster. It's a great way to help improve your health and manage your weight.

Himalayan Salt

Himalayan Salt comes in two forms: cooking salt and bath crystals. Regular table salt contains little to no value and can actually contribute to cellulite, rheumatism, arthritis, and kidney and gall stones. Himalayan Salt can help restore your balance and can be used in too many ways to mention here. Consult Mercola.com for more information.

Juicer, Omega 8003 and 8005 Models

I have done an extensive evaluation of juicers and found that the Omega 8003 and 8005 Juicers are the clear winners in terms of their multiple uses, durability, ease of use and cleaning, and value. You can find an extensive juicer evaluation chart comparing the various juicers at Mercola.com as well.

Kefir Starter and Culture Starter

Traditionally fermented foods are an essential part of every healthy diet, and the Kefir Starter and Culture Starter available on Mercola.com are an exceptionally high-quality way to make your own fermented foods very quickly and inexpensively. Kefir is an ancient health food (yet still one of nature's most powerful and delicious foods), and the Kefir Starter enables very easy preparation. The Culture Starter, meanwhile, is a simple way to make your vegetables into very healthy and delicious traditional fermented foods.

Salmon, Wild Red Alaskan and Toxin-Free

This Vital Choice brand of salmon is the *only* fish I have found, through independent laboratory testing we had performed on the fish, to be free from harmful mercury, PCBs, and other toxins. It is a premier source of omega-3 with EHA and DPA fatty acids, is high in antioxidants, and is free of antibiotics, pesticides, synthetic coloring agents, growth hormones, and GMOs. It also tastes absolutely incredible!

Foods—Other Suppliers

Herbs and Seasonings, Organic

Herbal Advantage, Inc., 1-800-753-9199
www.herbaladvantage.com

Milk and Cream, Raw
Go to www.realmilk.com to find out if there are cow-share programs in your area.

Nuts and Seeds, Raw and Organic
Jaffe Brothers Natural Foods, 1-760-749-1133, www.organicfruit-sandnuts.com

Spike®/ Salt-Free Spike
Famous all-purpose vegetable seasoning
Modern Products, 800-877-8935, www.modernfearn.com or in most grocery stores

Spouting Seeds, Organic
Complete line of organic seeds
The Sproutpeople, 877-777-6887, www.sproutpeople.com

Stevia
Non-carb, non-glycemic, non-synthetic, alternative sweetener
Available in liquid concentrate and baking powder
Body Ecology, 800-511-2660, bodyecologydiet.com

Kitchen Equipment—Other Suppliers

Food Dehydrators
Excalibur Dehydrator®
Excalibur Products, 1-800-875-4254, www.excaliburdehydrator.com

Juicers
See "Juicer, Omega 8003 Model," under "Recommended Products on Mercola.com"

Spiral SlicerTM
Manual slicer and processor for creating pasta from vegetables
www.takecontrolofyourhealth.com/resources

Sprouters
Sprouting equipment and seeds
The Sproutpeople, 1-877-777-6887, www.sproutpeople.com

Recommended Resources and Further Reading

Books

Nutrition and Physical Degeneration
Author: Dr. Weston Price

I often my refer patients to this wonderful resource. This is a pioneering work in natural health and simply a must-read if you are interested in the foundational truths of nutrition.

Dr. Westin Price was one of the most prominent dentists at the turn of the century and wondered why so many children were getting cavities. He realized that it was the introduction of processed foods. So, he traveled the world and documented the connection between processed foods and ill health. The principles he developed still largely hold true today.

Seeds of Deception
Author: Jeffrey M. Smith

If you're at all concerned about the safety of the food you're eating and serving to your family, I highly recommend this exceptional book. It's a shocking inside look into the frightening health dangers of genetically modified foods. Jeffrey M. Smith reveals the politics and corruption behind the biotech industry and why (despite the known dangers) these foods are allowed on the market.

Jeffrey M. Smith is a leading spokesperson on the health dangers of Genetically Modified Organisms (GMOs). He is the executive director of the Institute for Responsible Technology – a nonprofit organization committed to educating the public on the dangers of GMOs. Currently, Jeffery directs the Campaign for Healthier Eating in America, an industry and consumer movement to remove GMOs from the natural food industry.

Video and Audio Resources

Look for these video and audio health resources in the "Recommended Products" section of Mercola.com.

EFT Training Course

EFT is a profoundly effective emotional and mental healing approach based on the principles of energy medicine. I have taught it to the patients in my clinic for years, and they have experienced truly incredible and permanent results with it. Because EFT can help with everything (negative emotions, physical problems — it can even help you lower your golf score!) I think everyone can benefit from taking Gary Craig's "The EFT Course."

The EFT Course contains over 13 hours of video instruction. To learn more, please visit www.mercola.com/eft

Newsletters and Websites

Dr. Mercola's "eHealthy News You Can Use"
Subscribe at Mercola.com

My free newsletter (sent three times weekly) reaches one million subscribers as of this writing. This newsletter provides you with the most important and timely health news and information that can help you take control of your health and will also warn you of the deception and misinformation that is so prevalent in the health field.

Mercola.com

My website, with over 100,000 pages of useful articles and information on virtually any health topic you may be interested in, is now the world's most visited natural health website. Whenever you have a question about any health or dietary topic, simply go to Mercola.com and enter your search phrase in the powerful—and free—search engine.

You'll also find complete information about Nutritional Typing and how to obtain your Nutritional Type Assessment Test.

ENLITA.COM

ENLITA™ is an organization founded by Dr. Kendra Pearsall and Dr. Joseph Mercola to provide you with online education programs in specific areas of health and wellness. Our first program will focus on natural and holistic weight loss. If you want to discover how to attain your ideal weight with natural lifestyle changes, go to ENLITA.COM today.

The Weston A. Price Foundation

www.westonaprice.org

The Weston A. Price Foundation

A nonprofit organization founded in 1999. Their goals are to provide accurate information on nutrition and human health, including the vital importance of animal fats in the diet, and to provide the resources and information necessary to help people transition to a natural way of eating.

The Price-Pottenger Nutrition Foundation

www.price-pottenger.org

The Price-Pottenger Nutrition Foundation (PPNF) is another nonprofit organization whose main goal is to educate the public about the findings of Dr. Weston A. Price. They focus on disseminating the information gathered and researched by one of Price's better-known colleagues, Dr. Francis Pottenger. The discoveries of these two men have helped to form the basis of what we believe to be a truly healthy diet.

www.realmilk.com

A fantastic resource by The Weston A. Price Foundation providing everything you need to know about healthy raw milk. Includes detail on why raw milk is so nutritious, if its sales are legal in your regions, and where specifically to find cowshare programs or suppliers in your area.

Seeds of Deception Website

http://www.seedsofdeception.com/Public/Home/index.cfm

This website, created by Jeffery M. Smith, is an amazing resource for learning how you can become involved in raising awareness and instituting change against the use of genetically modified food. Here, you'll find additional information about the health dangers of GMOs and what you can do to get that information out into the world.

About The Authors:

Dr. Joseph Mercola is the founder of Mercola.com, the world's most visited natural health website. He is also the author of the 2006 book *Sweet Deception* and two New York Times bestsellers, *The Great Bird Flu Hoax*, and *The No-Grain Diet.*

As an osteopathic physician, Dr. Mercola first trained in conventional medicine and later received extensive training in natural medicine. He graduated medical school in 1982 at Midwestern University in Chicago. He has served as Chairman of the Department of Family Practice at St. Alexius Hospital in Illinois for five years and has been interviewed and profiled extensively for his health and dietary expertise, including New York Times, Wall Street Journal, Time Magazine, ABC's World News Tonight, CBS, ABC, NBC, Fox TV and CNN, and most recently on the Today Show.

Dr. Kendra Pearsall is a Naturopathic Physician who has specialized in natural weight loss ever since she graduated from Southwest College of Naturopathic Medicine in Tempe, Arizona in 2001. She is the co-author of *Dr. Mercola's Total Health Program*, *Sweet Deception* and *Dr. Mercola's Take Control Of Your Health* and is the medical editor of *The Hormone Handbook*. Pearsall's mission is to teach people how to achieve permanent weight loss through lifestyle changes with her weight loss and personal growth website: www.ENLITA.com. Pearsall's interests include researching health, politics and religion, world travel, spending time in nature, and creating a future health resort.

About Our Recipe Contributors

Karen Gilbert, a Certified Natural Chef and Certified Nutrition Educator, is a graduate of Bauman College in Sonoma County, California. Bauman College is a Holistic Nutrition and Culinary Arts school. In Karen's work as a chef and nutrition educator, she emphasizes the use of whole, organic, natural foods, nutritive herbs, and appropriate supplementation to relieve and restore metabolic balance. Karen's focus as a chef is the creation of delectable gourmet meals that also happen to be healthy and nutritious. As a nutrition educator, Karen emphasizes and informs her clients on the value of nutrition and assists them in creating original and innovative meals that are tailored to their specific nutritive needs. She understands the philosophy of healthy eating and is eager to show people how it can make a difference in how we feel, in disease prevention, and in over-all general health. Karen, a native Californian, has resided in Marin County for over fifteen years. She works in the Marin, Sonoma, and San Francisco Bay Area as a personal chef, private chef, and nutrition educator. She can be contacted at info@chefkarengilbert.com. For more information, visit www.chefkarengilbert.com.

Erin Fisher is a Certified Nutrition Educator and Certified Nutritional Consultant. She studied in Santa Cruz, California at California state-certified Bauman College: Holistic Nutrition and Culinary Arts (formerly IET). Erin is dedicated towards helping peo-ple improve their health and lives. She believes whole food nutrition is the foundation for optimal health. She prioritizes incorporating the whole person into her sessions: including lifestyle, mind, body, spirit, and energy. Erin has worked extensively within the health food and supplement industry for several years and finds a harmo-nious balance between working with clients and working within this field. Currently, Erin lives in Berkeley, CA.

Shobhan is originally from the UK and has been living in California for almost twenty-five years. Shobhan has been passionate about nutrition, food, and cooking for many years, and she trained at Bauman College in Berkeley, California to become a Nutrition Educator and Natural Chef. Shobhan has worked at Café Gratitude, San Francisco's premiere raw/vegan restaurant. She is currently work-ing as a personal natural chef, specializing in cooking for cancer patients. When Shobhan is not cooking, she spends much of her time working with children, singing, recording, writing songs, and performing live. Her e-mail is shomash@sbcglobal.net.